Moonshine Made Simple

Still Makers
Manual & Definitive Guide

Make genuine HokiNooki Moonshine

How to fabricate your own Still

Ferment your own Wash

Distill your own Spirit

Purification

Flavour

Taste

Gasohol for your Car

By Byron Ford

Copyright

Disclaimer

The author of this manual has presented the information herein in good faith, and to the best of his knowledge, the content is factual and free from gross error. However, the author assumes no responsibility or liability for any results or any conclusions that may be based in whole or part on this material. It is presented for the informational purposes only.

The law on freedom of information and speech make it possible to present this manual. What is described and discussed in this manual is illegal in some countries, according to the gods, when put into practice. So what the author intends is not to tempt the readers to break the law, but gain the knowledge for when the law allows one to purify their own alcohol by distillation. Atlas, from Greek Mythology, a giant, and one of the Titans, was condemned to bear the heavens upon his shoulders for rebelling against the gods. Home distillation is an interesting topic for discussion and acquiring such superior knowledge and skills is an effortless burden for you to bear, compared to that of Atlas.

Many, Many thanks To:

Peter Eastwood of Fermtech Wholesalers Ltd, New Zealand
> For his Superior skills in brewing and editing this manual.

Brian Nixon (Nicko) of Nicko's Brewtique, Nerang Queensland
> For his excellent knowledge and editing skills.

Lex Gordon Queensland for his experience and knowledge of brewing Rum.

© Byron Ford
Published by Fermtech Wholesalers Ltd, New Zealand

First Printing, Revision 2.0 - November 2000
Fonts used: Arial for most of the text.
Symbol and MS Reference 2 for symbols and fractions.

Contents

Contents

Contents

Contents

Contents

Preamble

About this Manual and Moonshine

Pure ethyl alcohol creation for personal consumption can be both satisfying and cost-effective as a leisure pursuit for those of you who live in countries that allow you to do so lawfully. Those of you who enjoy making beer and wine will find this manual particularly fascinating, as it is a logical expansion of your well-earned skills. Fermentation for spirits is identical, where sugar is turned into alcohol using yeast, but instead of consuming the brew, we subject it to some meticulous purification methods. This process is known as fractional distillation. This is a scientific system with which it is difficult to produce a failure. Crystal clear and clinically clean ethyl alcohol is produced every time, almost without a disaster. Even if your fermentation stage fails, or the distillation is disastrous, there are procedures for recuperation without ego injury.

This pure alcohol is diluted in the region of 40%, and then flavoured with essences or organic concoctions to create many of your fashionable beverages. As an example, you could mix up a concoction of herb and spices, add some juniper berries, and hey presto, you have made some London Dry Gin. Alternatively you could amble on down to your local brew shop to purchase some London Dry Gin essence, and then guess what, same end result. Some instant coffee and corn syrup with sugar will produce a wonderful after dinner liqueur that defies the taste of the original. It will be similar coffee liqueurs and great with coffee and mints.

If you enjoy tinkering around in your shed, you may take pleasure in the challenge of fabricating the scientific apparatus that is required to produce the fine spirit that is desired to create some of the exotic drinks that most people only dream about. There is not much plumbing or electrical aptitude required to create your very own unique apparatus.

All equipment described in this manual is constructed from food quality stainless steel, although, if manufactured from copper, it could resemble the original material used for distilling whisky in Scotland. The satisfactions that you achieve will include the knowledge that you can rest easily as to the purity of the spirit that you create. It will be extremely high quality and superior to many commercial manufacturers. So pure, those hangovers and headaches will be a dwindling memory, and the cost of production will be a fraction of the commercially retailed counterpart.

Even your failed wine that tastes of vinegar or old dog socks, or smells like a zoo keepers heel, can be re-processed into something that smells like a rose and tastes like nectar from the gods with a little care and experience.

Discussion on the Legal Side

In most countries it is not unlawful to publish, sell or purchase a book on producing Moonshine or amateur distillation, but in some countries it is prohibited to actually be involved in the production without a licence.

The grounding behind the laws is a little vague to say the least, unless remuneration is involved. Distillation is nothing but a course of action of purification from the result of fermentation. It doesn't actually make any alcohol, and is totally incapable of doing so. Amateur wine and beer makers are free to make as much alcohol as they desire for their own consumption. Therefore it is abundantly obvious that the law is based upon a completely false premise. Folks in New Zealand and Italy are among the countries that already enjoy the freedom to manufacture and distill alcohol at home for their own utilization. It is the endeavour of this publication to eventually make the distillation of alcohol achievable in more countries, in the homes of amateurs, in the same way to the making of beer and wine.

Introduction

Numerous books have been written on the production of beer and wine, home brew, but very little has gone to press about producing spirits at the level required by the amateur for home consumption. This manual attempts to enlighten those of you who are interested in this area under discussion. The emphasis is on the production of potable spirit, essential oils and equipment required to produce those products. A large section is dealt with on the apparatus and how to assemble such equipment as very little is written on home distillation paraphernalia.

Armed with the knowledge enclosed within this manual, you will stumble on how simple it is to make the very uncontaminated alcohol. Then you can produce a variety of beverages with superior quality and wholesomeness to those commercially obtainable. The price will be a small part of the price tag that you are accustomed to paying from the retailers. The explanation of how simple it is will become apparent as you step forward through this manual. We should not close our eyes to the vast array of alcoholic beverages that can be created. After all, the spirits and liqueurs in your grog cabinet all contain alcohol and some sort of flavouring to produce their unique appeal. Pretty well all of these can be reproduced nowadays with the obtainable essences.

Preamble

With some experimentation you can create some rather unique beverages yourself, which will amaze both you and your friends.

This manual will appeal to those of you who are knowledgeable in creation of alcohol, be it beer and wine, or distillation. It will also be of assistance to individuals engaged in the production of essential oils and potions to cure coughs, colds, sore soles and pimples in strange places.

The section on essential oils will also be of value for the extraction of flavours fundamental for the pioneers in search of a unique liqueur. As mentioned previously, juniper berries are required to create Dry Gin, if you are inclined not to use the obtainable flavourings. Extracting the bouquet and flavours from these berries is covered in the essential oils section.

There are comprehensive details on how to construct a crude wine from cane sugar and fractionally distill it to eliminate all the nasty impurities, thereby producing a clinically clean, pure alcohol. Instructions follow for flavouring and aging of your prized spirit, which incidentally can be an exceptionally short period of time.

A section on producing Moonshine from the fundamental raw materials not including sugar could be of interest to those who wish to duplicate the long-established Scottish tradition of whisky production. From this moonshine segment you can learn how to produce both Bourbon and Rye whiskeys using time-honoured methods and ingredients.

The measurement systems used in this manual are metric as there are differences in US Gallon and the imperial equivalents. The Tables and Reference Section on page 88 will help those who are not acquainted with the metric system. Some pipe measurements appear in imperial because they are universally recognized and available in most countries.

It was difficult to decide how much detail to incorporate as content in this manual because many similar publications tend to be full of gobbledygook that never gets to the area under discussion. Most of this manual is short and to the point with additional explanations further throughout the manual so that you can get started without too much preamble. It has been kept short and to the point so that you don't loose too much concentration. Some sense of humour has been included without being too political or regional to lighten up the content.

The section Conversion of a Pressure Cooker on page 66 is incorporated for those living in Australia, as it would appear that owning a 5 litre still for the manufacture of essential oils is legal at the time of writing this manual. Times could change in Australia and USA for the production of other products and larger, more convenient sized boiling vessels. So we must be at ease with the laws as they stand. Maybe some letters and publications will help enlighten those who are in the law and decision making positions of the countries in question.

Alcohol of Yesteryear

With risk of being tiresome, we will take a brief journey back in time. If that sounds real uninteresting, then skip this section because it is of little importance except for helping to fill up this page.

Once upon a time, in a far distant land, which is getting closer, there lived a race called the Ancient Chinese. It was these clever relations, as it was believed, to have been the first to unveil the secret of distillation. Unfortunately the efforts of producing alcohol from barley, rice and rye escaped documentation until relatively recently, around 800 BC. Although these records appear correct, it was thought that 4000 BC would be a better educated guess.

The better-refined documentation efforts of the Greeks, Egyptians and Arabs would date wine and beer distillation in Greece by Aristotle around 380 to 320 BC. The Arabs, around this time appeared responsible for this knowledge. It was thought that Japanese and Indochinese introduced this wisdom to the western world via Arabia. At this time, the European methods appeared to be fermentation of the grape. So wine was born that possibly tasted like muddy mouthwash that was filtered through the kidneys of a camel. It would appear that from around 500 BC the Greeks and Romans relished beer and wine.

A paper was written during the 10th century by the Spanish-Arabian physician Albucasis on the techniques of distillation of vinegar, water and wine. The year 1220 was the time when the Arabian alchemists introduced distillation to Italy. They must have refined it somewhat, as the Grappa produced to this day appears unaltered and is still very popular. It took till 1650 to spread throughout most of northern Europe.

The Irish and Scottish peasantry were soon to jump on to the bandwagon in the 1300's and it became a widespread and popular pastime throughout the population. It would arise that these two races were responsible for the introduction of distillation into USA, Australia and New Zealand.

The illicit potions produced by the Irish and Scottish peasants, who avoided taxes by a game of hide and seek, was far superior to that of the legitimate Whisky producers, and was cheaper to boot. To this day, the same situation exists among amateur still operators. That is, the production of exceptional and preferred spirits to educated.

Fragrant and Essential Oils

Olden Golden Oils

Physicians with an ancient knowledge of healing people with a process of gums and oils started distilling extracts around the times of the equally ancient alchemists who used bubbling retorts to search for methods of turning lead into gold.

Olive oil was often used as a base, into which was steeped the more expensive aromatic extracts. One of these was the ancient rare costly oil of spikenard that was collected from a plant that grew at high altitudes in many inaccessible mountains. This oil has mention in the Bible and was eagerly sort after by kings and queens. Other oil extracts became effective aids to health and healing. Seeking more concentrated formulas, the physicians turned to the process of distillation used by the alchemists, to extract the purer essential oils.

Early settlers leaving Europe, to take up roots in lands such as America and Australia, brought with them the knowledge and skills of their old ways, and even a few healing powders and oils. But alas, the previously known plants were left at home and they were faced with a completely foreign flora. Their knowledge from their deserted homeland would have been ineffectual for the construction of their potions until some knowledge was gained from the local tribal natives.

The increasing numbers of readily available off the shelf remedies, medicines and natural cures, and the utilisation of essential oils practically disappeared for the best part of the last century.

But in the last ten years there has been a phenomenal resurgence in the demand of fragrant and essential oils as modern scientific methods have been developed to replace the old alchemists methods of manufacturing. These new methods have been applied to traditional remedies, frequently with startlingly favourable results.

Potions, Perfumes and Splendid Oils

Pleasant fragrances were once essential in days gone by to disguise the foulness of unwashed bodies and living areas alike. Potpourris were made from many fragrant flowers and herbs that were close by. But there was a need for more powerful fragrances for disguise. This was particularly required outdoors, where folks were unable to carry enough mixes in their personal attaches to be of lasting benefit.

Scented sachets were once attached to dresses, pillows and stashed in beds, wardrobes and linen closets. This was the start of the popular use of fragrant waters prepared by steeping a mixture of flowers and gums into warm water or oils. Oils tended to prolong the fragrance by gradual evaporation into the atmosphere.

An amazing discovery was made. These fragrant waters became oily and the fine film of oil glistened on the surface. Linen cloth was employed to gather these essential oils. This was carefully squeezed into a small bottle or amphora. The effort required to collect as little as 25ml was immense, so it ensured that these extracts were sparingly applied, and valued extremely.

There was a two-fold benefit to the use of many essential oils. The reduction in body stench was wonderful, along with an even better effect. It was discovered that some oils gave marvellous recovery in the healing of wounds that benefited ones health, resulting in a reduction of the body's insect population and less body odour.

By the middle ages, many larger estates run by religious orders, and similar groups, implemented special grounds for growing therapeutic and/or fragrant plants.

Many still rooms were set aside, other than kitchens, in old houses and monasteries, for the extraction and distillation of the oils from gathered plants. This became a very responsible position for employment for one who had knowledge of alchemy and distillation. Many stills were in use to gather and concentrate this prized potion.

How do we Smell?

We smell just fine, thank you very much. When inhaling a scent, the odour molecules float to the back of the nasal cavity. Here they dissolve in the moist environment and unite with receptor or olfactory cells. These cells then trigger off electrical messages, via the nerve network, to the olfactory bulb in the brain. Most of the essential molecules, that have triggered the system, are breathed out, although some will enter the blood stream via the lungs. The cerebral cortex and limbic systems are the brain area that is concerned with smell messages. Many of our vital functions such as sleep, sexual drive, hunger, and thirst, as well as smell are handled by the limbic system. Also emotion and memory are handled by the same area and thereby link between smell, emotion and memory. Odours will fade when all the receptors are full, but will be vacated after 10 minutes or so. This explains why smells become unnoticed after a while but others will comment about them upon entering the room.

Home Production of Essentials

Nowadays there are tremendous outlets in the marketplace for the aforementioned oils and potions. There is no secret for the methods employed to extract these essences. Your own basic oils can be created with some inexpensive equipment available on today's market.

The type of essences that are able to be produced in your own home include alcohols, esters and oils, each of which have a distinct fragrance or healing property. Many trees and shrubs have a different fragrance in early morning compared to late in the afternoon. A fuller heavier aroma is usually apparent after the higher temperatures are experienced in late afternoon.

Chemically, the tender, lighter fractions with a lower vapour temperature are evaporated and removed from the original mixture before the heavier elements that need higher temperatures. Nature does not oblige for the collection of fragrances for perfume houses of the higher and lower tones required. But the distiller's art can capture the complete, or part thereof, fragrances by varying the temperature at which the collection is made of the different fractions of oils. When we have fractioned an oil by splitting it into many temperature zones for collection, we can recreate the perfume of a rose, to our desire, by leaving out the some of the scents that we do not like.

Enter, the modern day Alchemist

Over hundreds of years we have learned the basic methods of extracting fragrances and essential oils from many different woody materials and adapted them to modern day equipment. Before we totally destroy an unknown bush by denuding it of all its limbs and leaves. We can crush a handful of flowers or leaves, mix them into some warm water, and place them in a bowl with a lid, then keep it in a refrigerator overnight or up to 24 hours.

We then perform the tasks that the alchemists of old completed. Take a look to see if there is any oily film present floating on the surface of the water. A heavy oil slick would indicate a high potential yield. If there is no oil slick, don't be disheartened. This may prove that the fragrance that you were chasing is actually dissolved in the solution. There may have been no oils in this collection for distillation.

You may use any fragrant or gummy wood, resinous leaves or fragrant flowers. One thing that you should remember is that the lighter fragrances will be more troublesome to capture. Once you have distilled your potion, it may appear a little cloudy. Just keep collecting your potions until you have enough to re-distill to concentrate the solution. This method is more favourable to that of using expensive chemicals that are often used commercially. Freezing the water out of your lighter fragrances is a useful method. After freezing, you can carefully collect near pure oil that is poured away from the frozen water.

Blending of Fragrances

Try blending your precious collections together with other plant oils, which themselves may be fragrant or useful in health improvement. You may try Olive, Almond, Corn or Peanut oils as carrier oil, especially for massage purposes. Water can be used for many fragrances and colognes. Keep your blend at a low percentage. Maybe less than 5% essential oils mixed with other carrier oils would work well. Fragrant perfumes maybe up to 15% or 30% of your collected oils mixed with water or other oils. Colognes could be between these two. Whether you use other oils or water depends mainly upon the type of extract that you end up with. Remember it is difficult to mix water and oils together. This is where alcohol can be employed, as it will mix with many oils.

When testing, apply a little to a non-sensitive part of you body before splashing it around. This will give you indication if your potion has any disastrous effects. Some people have more sensitive skin than others. So be careful. Do some research first, especially if you intend to take your Potpourri's internally. Please remember that some of your sweet smelling fragrances may be highly poisonous, so do some research.

Lavender, citrus, and eucalyptus would a fairly safe bet to start with. They are used in many commercially available oils. Tea Tree oil is often used as an antiseptic solution for dingo bites or goanna gouges, but others may be favourable to complement your dwindling love life.

Getting Down to Essential Oil Production

Most essential oils are produced by distillation or expression. Generally, because of the fragile nature of the raw material, the process takes place in the country of origin. We will discuss three basic methods of distillation. Water dissolvable, Steam dissolvable and Alcohol dissolvable oils. Always collect the freshest materials that are available and store them in sealed bags in the fridge. A mincer or solidly built food processor can be employed to crush your stash. Steeping can be easily prepared by soaking macerated material in warm water in an airtight container. Resinous material may take some days to extract completely while soft flowers take just 24 to 48 hours.

- **Water dissolvable oils.** Floral water is a product of this method of distillation. Soak your newly collected materials, that were crushed and containing the essential oils, in warm water for 24 to 48 hours. Strain off the solids, keeping only the water and oil mixture. Add this liquid to the pot of your still and set it up ready for distillation. Bring it to the boil; making sure that there is enough water flowing through the still to condense any steam that appears from the condenser. Collect your potion in 50 to 100ml quantities. Test each batch before combining them to ensure that your quality is acceptable according to odour etc. The character of these fractions will vary somewhat as the condensate is driven off. Quit the distillation after there are no more oils or odours.

- **Steam dissolvable oils.** With this process, the steam causes the glands containing the essence to burst, allowing the volatile chemicals to dissolve in the steam. This rises and is taken into the condenser, where it is cooled. As it cools, the oils may become separated from the water. Fill the pot of your still to just below its maximum capacity. Then suspend the collected and crushed materials containing the oils over the water in a wire basket. Or sit it on small blocks above the water on a wire mesh screen. Replace the still head and condenser. Close the still, ensuring that all hoses and fittings are secure. Bring the still to the boil and collect the condensate as it emerges from the condenser. As the steam passes through your stash in the basket, it will pick up the oils/fragrances and carry them through with the condensate. Keep enough water flowing through the still condenser to arrest any escaping vapour from the outlet. As above, collect your brew in 50 to 100ml batches for later sampling and blending. Before blending, make sure that the odour is to your liking of collected batch, as they will vary somewhat.

- **Alcohol dissolvable Oils.** Solvent extraction using alcohol is favoured for releasing essential oil from more delicate material, such as jasmine flowers. Soak the newly crushed material, that was stored in your refrigerator containing the oils, in a solution of 50%/V ethyl alcohol for 24 to 48 hours. Place the potion back in your fridge for that duration. This should allow the oils to separate from your crushed stash. Strain off the remaining solids, keeping just the liquid of alcohol and water containing the essential oils. Add this liquid to the still pot, making sure that there is enough of this liquid so that it does not boil dry. Assemble your still as before and bring it to the boil. Make sure that there is enough water flowing through your still so that all the escaping steam will condense. Collect your solution in 100ml batches as before for later blending. Also, you can try a reduced percentage of alcohol in the pot by adding the same volume of water to your alcohol. Be careful, alcohol is flammable. Production of alcohol is covered in depth later in this manual. Oil made by this process is known as an absolute.

By now you should have the first of your essential oils. The first production will be priceless whether it is first-rate or appalling. However, if it smells like a Zoo keepers heel rather than a rose, try again, this time keep cool, keep tight and out of sight, until your success has been achieved. Remember that you are creating something unique and will definitely improve with experience and time. There are many books on essential oils explaining what plants are useful, and for what purpose. It is not within the scope of this manual to explain these points. What we are trying to cover is the extraction methods that are not enclosed within these other manuals and publications.

Although some commercial productions frequently involve pressing and solvent extraction, we suggest that only water and or alcohol should be used for the sake of safety. Most of the solvents used are extremely flammable and exude dangerous fumes, not to mention the ability to be absorbed by the skin, and possibly kill you.

Diluting your essential oils delays their entrance and passage through your body, but does not detract from the efficiency of the essential oils. After treatment the essential oils remain in your body for three or four hours or more, activating the healing process, which can continue for two or three weeks.

Essential oils are able to influence all aspects of the body's functions, from tissues to organs, to body fluids and cells, as well as our emotional state and the spiritual aspects of the person.

Some plants employed for potions extraction

Herbs	Flowers	Leaves	Fruit/Seed	Wood
Thyme	Rose	Eucalypt	Citrus Peel	Eucalypt
Mints	Lavender	Catnip	Aniseed	Macrocarpa
Rosemary	Jasmine	Juniper Berries	Sandalwood	Sandalwood
Peppermint	Pennyroyal	Lemongrass	Camphor	

It has been known to process marijuana seeds, stalks and leaves into other products using distillation. At this time, no comment is appropriate.

Most of the above material will be finely shredded, mulched or crushed. Then they will be steeped in warm water overnight, or longer for woods, and then distilled when ready. Sometimes you will distill and collect up to one third of the original volume poured into the still pot. Be careful not to let the still pot boil dry. Measure the volume that you poured in and compare it with what you get out. In this way you will be able to establish how much is retained within the boiling pot during the distillation process. Combine these batches and re-distill if necessary to further purify your collection. Freezing your potion in your refrigerator can separate the milky distillates. Once frozen, the oils will separate from the water and can be poured out. The remaining water can be used once combined with your next batch.

The alcohol necessary for extracting some of your oils is fully covered in the next few sections of this manual.

Using Herbs and Essentials Wisely

Commonly used herbs and essential oils are extremely safe to use. However, some plants can produce side effects, and like all medicines, herbal remedies and essential oils alike, must be treated with respect. It is essential to take or use certain plants only under the guidance of a well-trained practitioner, to avoid adverse consequences. Ephedra (*Ephedra sinica*) for example, can be extremely toxic at the wrong dosage, and comfrey (*Synphytum officinale*), a very popular herb in the past, is thought to cause severe or even fatal liver damage in rare circumstances. When herbal medicine is used correctly, however, the chances of developing a serous side effect are remote. Also these herbs are taken internally.

Another instance is Tea Tree oil, from the *Melaleuca alternifolia* tree, although extremely fine medicinal sterilising and antiseptic oil should never be taken internally without medical advice. It would currently be one of the most popular essential oils for external use.

Alcohol Production

Stock required for making alcohol

The stock required for the production of alcohol is only sugar and water plus some bakers yeast or turbo yeast. It is covered in the section Fermenting the Alcohol Wash on page 13.

Fermentation

Fermentation is the process required for the production of alcohol from sugar, water and yeast. It is covered in the sections Fermenting the Alcohol Wash on page 13 and Understanding Fermentation 40, both of these sections will be helpful.

Distillation

Distillation is the procedure required extracting the alcohol from your fermented Wash of fermented sugar using yeast and water. You will find sections under Distillation on page 19 and Distillation Discussion on page 44 both helpful.

Filtering & Dilution

Filtering and dilution of your alcohol is necessary to obtain pure and odour free spirit. Carbon Purification on page 23 and Making Spirits and Liqueurs on page 24 covers these two subjects. Also the section on Purification System on page 70 will expand your knowledge on this essential subject.

Flavouring

Flavouring of your beverage is the final stage of production. At this stage you will make your squeaky clean spirit into a beverage that you will enjoy. It is covered in the section under Making Spirits and Liqueurs on page 24.

Getting Started

There is no requirement that you gain an immense amount of knowledge to get started in home distillation. Just follow the instructions from the following page, to the section Making Spirits and Liqueurs on page 24, and just browse at the rest until you have gained some experience. Then the later sections of this manual will finely hone your knowledge to the extent that you will become a highly experienced brewer and distiller.

Fermenting the Alcohol Wash

The term Wash that is used in the following text refers to the mixture of nutrients, sugar, water and yeast fermented to produce alcohol.

Equipment Required

- **Fermentation Vessel:** A plastic bucket with a removable lid makes an ideal vessel for fermentation. The lid can be a push fit or screw on type, but must be airtight. It should be of a white translucent material so that you can view the contents from the outside. You will probably require a 30-litre vessel to ferment a 25-litre Wash. There must be greater than 100mm space between the top of the Wash and the lid to allow for frothing and expansion. The plastic should be of food grade material and clean from any previous contents without any odour. Such vessels are very easy to keep clean. You will need to punch a hole in the lid to allow mounting a Fermentation Lock. A tap mounted near the bottom of this vessel is a good idea for the removal of the Wash after fermentation. There are adhesive thermometers available that you can stick on the side of your fermentation vessel to indicate the temperature of your Wash. You should mark the side of your fermentation vessel at the 25-litre point. Calibrate this by pouring in 25 litres of water and mark it at that point.

- **Fermentation Lock:** The fermentation lock should be of a clear plastic material, containing a water trap that allows ventilation of carbon dioxide, but prevents the Wash coming in contact with the outside air. The carbon dioxide, which is heavier than air, is generated during the fermentation process and protects the Wash from air.

- **The Siphon:** Siphons should be of a plastic material, as rubber tubes can cause peculiar flavours if used with alcohol. The siphon is used for transferring the finished Wash to the distillation vessel. It should have a spacer on the bottom of the tube so that about 20mm of the deposit is left behind in the fermentation vessel during siphoning. Some fermentation vessels have a tap mounted around 20mm from the bottom to allow for transferring the fermented Wash via a plastic tube.

- **Hydrometer:** A hydrometer is not entirely necessary, but will help you understand and fine-tune your fermentation process. A wine and beer hydrometer that has a specific gravity range from 980 to 1150 would be extremely useful.

Sterilising Your Equipment

Cleaning: Normal household liquid detergent is perfect for washing up all your brewing equipment and utensils. Any stubborn stains can be removed using 50gr of Sodium Metasilicate (brews detergent) mixed with 5 litre of water. Be sure to remove all traces of cleaning agents before fermentation is attempted, as these can cause contamination.

Every piece of equipment should be clean and sterilised before and after use. This includes the fermentation vessel, fermentation lock, siphon, hydrometer and a paddle for stirring, even your stainless utensils.

Sterilising: Many different types of sterilising chemicals can be used including Sodium Metabisulphite, Sterophos (pink stain remover) and Chlorine. All traces of these chemicals must be removed by rinsing with cold water several times before use commences. After rinsing, seal the fermentation vessel to prevent contamination. Dilute a cup of household bleach Sodium Hypochlorite (chlorine bleach) in 5Ltr of water and sterilise all your equipment including spoons and cutlery. Dismantle and soak all bungs and taps as well. Even your workbench should be sterilised. Sterophos is also an ideal product for cleanup and sterilisation.

Mixing Procedure

In principle, Wash is a cheap wine with no demands concerning taste. Only alcohol product is required, without any fusel oils. Therefore a clean, impurity free Wash is essential to give good results. The purest and most simple Wash is comprised of sugar or dextrose and yeast with a yeast nutrient, fermented in pure water. The yeast consumes the sugar and nutrients to produce both carbon dioxide and ethyl alcohol.

Because there are many different types of yeast available we will discuss two types only. We will assume that we are going to make a 25Ltr brew. You can scale up or down all quantities and weights to suit yourself. Because of heat problems, it is unadvisable to exceed 200 Litres per brew. Without proper heat control, even the most experienced brewers will have difficulties.

- **Turbo Yeast:** There are many turbo yeasts available from brew shops and they vary in the amount of alcohol that they can produce before becoming inactive. Look for one that can produce close to 20% alcohol from your Wash. There are usually instructions on the yeast packets that will guide you as to the quantity of sugar that can be used. Normally all the required yeast nutrients are included in the pack. Turbo yeast generally makes a cleaner brew than bakers' yeast so they are definitely preferred.

- **Bakers' Yeast:** This is your standard type of yeast that can produce a maximum of 13% alcohol from your Wash before the yeast becomes inactive. In order to feed the yeast, and reduce the production of fusel oil, we should add yeast nutrients. The most important nutrient for yeast is nitrogen. Usually one adds 25 to 50 grams of ammonium carbonate or ammonium phosphate for the fermentation of 25Ltr Wash. So you can mix together 5 grams of dry bakers' yeast with 25 grams of yeast nutrient. Depending on the quality of the yeast, in most cases this should make a good mixture for a 25Ltr Wash.

- **Believe me**, Turbo Yeast is by far the easiest method used today.

The amount of sugar required would depend on the type of yeast that you are using. Bakers yeast will produce a maximum of 14% alcohol, but we will assume 13%. Some turbo yeasts will produce 20% alcohol from your Wash. If we use normal granular white sugar we can use a formula to establish the amount of sugar required. 17 grams of white sugar will produce 1% of alcohol in one litre of Wash. So therefore we can calculate the amount of sugar that is required, according to the yeast that we choose, as follows. (17 grams of sugar can produce 10ml of alcohol.)

Bakers' yeast to produce 13% alcohol.

% Alcohol		17gr sugar		25Ltr Wash		
13	x	17	x	25	=	5525 Grams

Turbo yeast that can produce 20% alcohol

20	x	17	x	25	=	8500 Grams

We normally use 5Kg of sugar for bakers' yeast, or 8Kg for turbo yeast capable of producing 20% alcohol in a 25Ltr Wash.

If you wish to experiment with dextrose instead of sugar, just multiply your sugar weight by 1.125 (+1/8th). So 8Kg of sugar becomes 9Kg of dextrose (5Kg becomes 5.6Kg). Dextrose tends to make a cleaner Wash, but more expensive to purchase. Many folks will use only dextrose once tried.

From the above calculation, mix your quantity of sugar thoroughly with 5Ltr of boiling water, making sure that all sugar is totally dissolved. If the sugar is not entirely dissolved, it cannot be converted into alcohol. Add this to your empty sterilised fermentation vessel. Now add cold chlorine free tap or rainwater to bring the volume up to the 25Ltr mark.

Quickly heat or cool the Wash temperature to between 18° and 25° Celsius, add your yeast as soon as possible, and mix in thoroughly. Preferably start your yeast at the cooler temperature because the yeast will raise the temperature as fermentation commences. You can lower the temperature by immersing a frozen plastic bottle of water into the Wash. Frozen copper rods can also be used for this purpose. Close the lid of your fermentation vessel and insert the fermentation lock. Add water to the lower part of the air lock, to inhibit the entry of air and insects.

The fermentation lock prevents air coming in contact with Wash. If this happens, the oxygen and bugs in the air may oxidise the alcohol into acetic acid. During fermentation the carbon dioxide, which is heavier than air, protects the Wash like a protective cover. This again is a good reason to leave greater than 100mm of space between the Wash surface and the fermentation cover. Within 24 hours, carbon dioxide should start bubbling through the air lock. That is if the brew is working correctly and the fermentation vessel is correctly sealed.

If the Wash becomes too hot (Over 40° C), the yeast may be killed or weakened, and therefore unable to ferment out all the sugar.

If there are <u>no bubbles</u> exiting from the air lock, loosen the top of the fermentation vessel so that you can have a quick look inside. The Wash should have fine bubbles and will probably have froth on top. A vigorous agitation with a plastic paddle may speed up fermentation.

The Wash needs to ferment between 18° and 25° Celsius for about one week. If the fermentation lock ceases to bubble, the Wash may be fully worked out. Slightly higher temperature could possibly reduce the fermentation time if cell death is not event, but will produce some unwanted by-products. A lower temperature will usually take longer to fully ferment out and produce a cleaner reliable brew.

In cooler weather the temperature could drop too low and fermentation may cease, so a heating pad can be used to keep the Wash warm. Do not use a heating pad for the 1st 24 to 48 hours. Heating pads should be available from your brew shop.

Fermentation is complete when all the sugar is used up in the production of alcohol and carbon dioxide. Bubbling should have stopped. If in doubt, leave the Wash for an extra day or two. You can drop your hydrometer into the Wash to measure the specific gravity. It ought to read 990 near the top of the scale, which is nearly submerged. Remember that your hydrometer is a delicate instrument and easily damaged.

In case of difficulty

If the fermentation vessel is not sealed correctly, the air lock will not bubble within 24 hours. Ensure that the lid is correctly sealed. Check the seal by lightly pressing the lid of the fermentation vessel to force some air out through the airlock.

After releasing the pressure, the air should return back through the air lock. If sealed properly, the water level in the air lock will remain uneven.

In cooler weather, the yeast may stop working before all the sugar is used. This would be indicated on your hydrometer reading being higher than 990. Any hydrometer reading greater than 1005 specific gravity suggests that something has gone wrong. In most cases, a vigorous stir should get the yeast working again, but in some cases you may need to add another batch of yeast. Possibly moving your brew to a warmer position and a good stir up will get it going again. An inexpensive stick-on thermometer, available from your local brew shop, will help monitor the temperature situation.

Adding more sugar to get the fermentation going again is a trick that a beer brewer may use. Unfortunately this is not such a good idea for alcohol brews of sugar and water. When you set down your brew, the sugar level was calculated so it would be completely exhausted at the same time as the yeast quits. The alcohol content has peaked, disabling the yeast. This is not only wasteful but can lead to frothing in the boiling vessel during distillation. It will also mess up your hydrometer readings.

Too much unfermented sugar will cause frothing during distillation. If frothing occurs, it will manifest itself by bubbles and cloudy liquid emerging at the spirit outlet of your still head. Shut down the heat source and remove the thermometer bung carefully to avoid scalding. This is a dangerous process. Now you can drop in around 3ml of Distilling Conditioner followed by a small amount of water, washing it into the boiling vessel. These still conditioners are a silicon antifoam emulsion that is available from a food processing chemical company or from some brew shops. Replace the rubber bung, carefully, and resume the heat source. Many folks will use Distilling Conditioner as a matter of course, as prevention is better than cure for the minimal cost that is involved.

Remember that turbo yeasts capable of producing a high yield of alcohol say 20%, are special high alcohol-tolerant yeasts. They will take longer to completely ferment. Allow 1 to 2 weeks at a liquid temperature not exceeding 25°C.

A profile of cool temperature of 18°C at the onset of fermentation, so that it is not too vigorous during the earlier stages, is desirable. This would be especially true for the use of Turbo Yeast. You can regulate your temperature by watching the activity in the fermentation lock. Keep it cool when the activity is high. A slow steady and stable bubbling is preferable to vigorous activity through the air lock.

Following Fermentation

It is undesirable to transfer yeast cells into the still pot as they can burst when subjected to heat and produce some foul smelling chemicals. Bad odour and colour can spoil an otherwise excellent spirit.

After fermentation, the alcohol content will be sufficiently high so that you can place your Wash in storage for a while. Remember to keep it sealed otherwise some acid forming bacteria will invade, converting your carefully produced ethanol into acetic acid (vinegar). If kept airtight in a cool place, your Wash can be kept for up to 3 weeks. Keeping it for longer than this time, standing on its bottom-deposits (lees), can cause souring of the Wash or oxidation.

After the Wash is fully fermented, it is desirable to let it settle to minimise the amount of yeast being transferred to the still. Cooling the Wash will speed the process of settling and clearing; it's just a question of waiting a few days. A refrigerator would be useful for this process.

To speed up the process, a clearing agent (finings) such as bentonite can be used. Mix this by slowly adding 25ml (25gr) of bentonite to 25ml of water. Beat briskly with a fork or whisk until completely assimilated. Let the mixture thicken for between 12 to 24 hours. Now vigorously mix this into your 25Ltr Wash and let it stand until completely cleared. This is common practice in wine making.

Another clearing agent is isinglass liquid finings available from Brew Shops. The approximate dosage is 10ml to 25Ltr Wash. This is a favourite among the beer brewers. Turbo Clear is another product that is especially produced for clearing spirit Wash fermentation.

A good habit is to siphon off the Wash into another vessel, leaving the yeast deposit behind. Then add your clearing agent if required. After clearing, the crystal clear Wash can be carefully siphoned into the distillation pot, ready for distillation. The bottom deposits (lees) are then discarded.

Note: Some research indicates that a clear or cloudy Wash will produce first-class spirit, especially when good activated carbon filtering is involved and a Reflux Still is used. Dextrose Wash will often produce a clearer result than that of sugar, but at an extra cost. Most people use white household granular sugar without any problems. Many of those who use dextrose will use nothing else.

Distillation

Brief Discussion on Distillation

Distillation is the process that we use to collect the alcohol from our fermented Wash. We will heat up the Wash to the boiling point of alcohol and cool down the steam (condensation) back to a liquid. Alcohol has a lower boiling point (78.3°C) than water (100°C) and so boils off first. This process will separate the alcohol from the Wash. The highest possible strength of ethyl alcohol that we can retrieve is approximately 95% (Max. 97.2%) and 5% water because this mixture boils at 78.15°C (below pure alcohol). This is called an azeotrope. The worst that we can say about an azeotrope is that they are difficult to spell or pronounce and they will not concern us at this point.

Because both alcohol and water will have some vapour pressure during distillation, there will always be some water going into vapour along with the ethanol. But until there is little ethanol left in our Wash, a good quality still will retrieve mostly ethanol. So we will collect alcohol around 78 to 85°C, until there is little left in our Wash, then there will be a sharp rise in the temperature to that approaching boiling water at 100°C.

We should never let our temperature exceed 90°C because this is where the headache materials called fusel oils start appearing. At this temperature there will be little ethanol left in our Wash, so shut down the still by removing the heat source.

Equipment Required

Distillation Apparatus (Still)

There are many Stills available, so here we will discuss the Reflux type of Still. A Reflux Still is essentially a two stage fractionating still. It will give you a greater purity of alcohol than a single stage still (Pot Still). The temperature is measured at the top of the Reflux Column. This is the first stage that removes all heavier fractions (water, fusel oils and other undesirable products). The remaining lighter fractions will then pass into the 2nd stage, which is known as the Condenser. From the condenser, you will receive your alcohol. A preferred material for manufacturing a still is food grade stainless steel. You can read more about this subject in the section Distillation Discussion on page 44 and Making Your Own Still on page 58.

Distillation Pot (Boiling Vessel)

The distillation pot can take on a variety of shapes and sizes. In some countries, this pot should not exceed a Wash size of 5 Litres. The most economical size for our Wash is a pot that can contain a 25Ltr Wash capacity. Stainless Steel is the preferred material. There should be greater than 100mm space between the Wash and lid/top to allow for expansion and frothing. The lid should have a seal to inhibit the escape of heated vapour. The still will be mounted on the lid of this pot. Many people have converted a pressure cooker for this purpose. Others have welded two stainless buckets or bowls together or used a converted 30Ltr water-heating urn. It can contain an integral heating element. These types are preferred for efficiency. A large removable lid is preferred for cleaning. Making a Boiling Vessel on page 66 will be worth reviewing.

Thermometer

A thermometer's most important task is to monitor the temperature at the top of the reflux column during distillation. It must be accurate around 78°C and finely calibrated in whole degrees. Some thermometers are accurate only when 2/3rd submersed in liquid. You need one that is accurate when only the bulb is submersed. Check its accuracy in boiling water (100°C) and make allowances.

Heat Source for the Still

If your distillation pot already contains a heating element, then discard this section.

You can use both gas and electric heating for modern day stainless steel stills. In the interest of safety, electricity is preferred to the open flame. A cook top hotplate on your oven is widely used and will have adjustable heat settings. Gas flames are often easier to obtain the correct heat setting, but remember that alcohol is extremely flammable. We don't want you to destroy all your windows or house.

Alcometer or Spirit Hydrometer

The alcoholic strength of a distillate is measured by an alcometer. It will only be accurate in pure mixtures of alcohol and water. Graded from 0 to 100%, the alcoholmeter functions in a similar manner to that of a hydrometer and it should be allowed to float on the surface of the spirit. It is temperature sensitive and can be checked for accuracy when floated in pure water at the manufacturers recommended temperature. The reading should be 0% alcohol. A 250 to 300mm length is desirable for accuracy.

Measuring Glass

For a 300mm alcometer or hydrometer a 250ml graduated glass cylinder is suitable. It should be graduated in millilitres so that it becomes useful when mixing and blending your spirits. A simple plastic tube will work well if it is tolerant to alcohol in high concentrations.

Distillation Procedure

The Wash should be transferred to the distillation pot using a siphon without disturbing the lees in the bottom of the fermentation vessel. This pot must not be filled up to the top, allow greater than 100mm space for expansion and frothing during boiling. Situate the complete still on a firm heat resistant base close to a cold water tap, drain and power socket.

Assemble your still and connect up the cooling water. Fill the still condenser and reflux section with cooling water and stop it from running when filled. Attach a small length of plastic hose to the spirit outlet of the still. The other end of this hose is just inside a collecting bottle or jug. Make sure that this hose is positioned so that no spirit can accumulate in any part, and the outlet cannot become submerged during filling. This hose must not have any constrictions, as there could be a build up of pressure within the still causing erratic or dangerous operation. All spirit must be able to flow freely. Make sure that the still pot lid is secure and cannot leak. Insert your thermometer using a rubber bung into the top of your reflux column. The complete bulb of the thermometer should protrude through the bung by at least 10mm. Your still is now ready for action.

Plug in your heat source and energise. The still will take some time to heat up to operating temperature. When the thermometer reads 50°C, start the cooling water flowing at 500ml per minute. Check this by collecting the water outlet in a calibrated jug for one minute. Turn down the heat source and watch the temperature, it should slowly increase to around 65°C.

At 65°C, you may have some spirit starting to flow. This is possibly some aldehydes and methanol. You can put this to good use as window cleaner or excellent fondue fuel or starter fluid for the barbecue. Now set the temperature at the column head by roughly setting the heat source and fine adjustment of the cooling water so that it climbs towards 78°C. Collect the first 100ml from your 25Ltr Wash and discard it or use it as cleaner. These are the fore shots (heads) and potentially headache materials so discard it as a precaution. Methylated Spirits is contained in the first few ml and we do not want to drink that do we.

The outlet of the cooling water should be quite warm, say around 40 to 50°C, not hot enough to scald your hand. The outlet of the spirit should be cool, not warm. The setting of the cooling water is very dependent on the water supply temperature, so the 500ml flow rate mentioned above is just an arbitrator starting point.

Your most important task now is to watch the temperature on your thermometer. It should be around 78°C, may be a little lower to start with.

Sample your spirit occasionally straight from the still by using your alcometer. Depending on how much heat that is applied to your boiling vessel, the reading should be around 80% alcohol or higher. Too much heat and the reading will be lower. The cooler that you can run your still; the higher will be the percentage of alcohol and the better the quality. We usually allow the temperature to range from 75 to 85°C.

Once the temperature reaches 89 to 90°C, check the spirit strength being condensed with your alcometer by taking your sample directly from the condenser outlet. Smell it for any unpleasant odour. If the strength is below 50% or the temperature is around 90°C or an unpleasant odour exists, you may consider halting production. Never ever exceed 92°C because you will run the risk of collecting fusel oils; this is definite headache substance. They produce a foul odour and some times appear visibly, floating on top of your distilled spirit. Normally fusel oil is only visible when the alcohol content is very low as high alcohol content has the ability to dissolve the unwanted fusels and become un-noticed.

By now, you should have about 5.5 to 6.5Ltr of spirit at around 60 to 70% alcohol, depending on the sugar concentration and type of Turbo Yeast employed during fermentation.

Remove the source of heat, and then carefully remove the hose connected to the spirit outlet of you Still Condenser and avoid being scalded by the escaping steam. Air must be allowed into the vessel, otherwise the resultant vacuum can cause the boiling vessel to implode and take on the look of a stainless steel rag. Allow the apparatus to cool.

Discard the Wash when it has cooled. Rinse out the vessel and reverse rinse the column and condenser. Use standard household detergent when washing the boiling vessel, column and condenser.

Carbon Purification - Not Optional

There are many methods to purify your spirit. It is the most important part of the entire manufacturing process. But it will not save a brew that failed proper distillation or was made from incorrect ingredients. So if you have ended up with a smelly or cloudy spirit, dilute it 1 to 1 with water, and redistill it over again. This time, more carefully.

This method of purification is by far the simplest one to get you started, and the grade of activated carbon that you require is 12X40 or close to that. Your brew shop can oblige with the correct type. We use 25 grams per litre of diluted spirit. The spirit should be diluted down to less than 50% with pure water. Use your alcometer to establish the strength.

Please remember that aquarium carbon will not do as it is made from impure substances not designed for use with products intended for human consumption, and will introduce rather nasty trace elements and flavours to your hard earned product. Properly sourced activated charcoal is now readily available from winemakers suppliers, specifically designed for the purpose of cleaning and polishing spirits.

Purification Procedure

Dilute your high-octane spirit that is above 50% down to 50%. We can establish the amount of water required by a simple calculation.

Litres collected **X** Alcohol strength ÷ Desired strength = Total

6.5Ltr **X** 70 ÷ 50 = 9.1Ltr Total after dilution.
Therefore 9.1 - 6.5 = 2.6Ltr of water required to be added to our original spirit. This is a rough guide only. Check it with your alcometer before adding all the water.

Calculate the amount of activated carbon required. 25gr per litre **X** 9.1Ltr = 227.5 Grams. We can round this to 225gr. The amount of activated carbon calculated here is on the high side just in case you are landed with a low-grade carbon.

You can use your fermenting vessel to purify your spirit. Pour in your 9.1Ltr of spirit, followed by 225gr of activated carbon. Stir vigorously every night and morning for 7 days. Then allow it to settle. A cool place will help to speed up the settling time.

Siphon off the clear spirit into a glass demijohn for storage. Now carefully filter the rest of the spirit through a coffee filter paper and add that to your demijohn for storage. Throw away your spent carbon.

Note: Your Brew Shop may advise you on better methods of purification.

Making Spirits and Liqueurs

We will assume that you are making up a 1.125Ltr bottle of Bourbon at 37% alcohol from your spirit that you diluted to 50%. Firstly, purchase the Bourbon essence from your brew shop. There are many different types to choose from.

We now calculate the quantity of 50% alcohol spirit required producing 37% final product by using the following formula.

Required strength **X** Volume required ÷ Original strength

37 **X** 1125ml ÷ 50 = 832.5ml of 50% spirit.

Pour the essence into an empty bottle. Follow the essence bottle instructions for the amount. Now add the 832ml of 50% spirit. Shake the bottle. Top up with pure water and shake again, then cap the bottle.

Aging process is simple for home made Bourbon. Storing it for a week or two will enhance the flavour. Some people will age their spirit for 6 to 8 weeks. You will notice the difference.

Most liqueurs require special attention. Many demand the addition of sugar and corn syrups (glucose) to thicken and enhance the sensation. Others will benefit from a small amount of glycerine for a better mouth feel. You can also use burnt sugar or caramel to add both darkening and fullness of taste to your spirit. Rum can be tweaked by the addition of a little cane sugar molasses and citrus such as orange and lemon including skins.

Fortifying to produce Port can be rewarding. Choose a favourite red wine and add 200mls of corn syrup to thicken and 450mls of 40% spirit to 400mls of red wine. Even a good Chateau Cardboard will work well.

The commercial spirit industries use many essences to flavour their products. This is a very common practice but little known by the general public. Such essences are of high quality and impart an excellent flavour and now available to the public for home brewers. The technology is advancing at a very high pace, giving products of quality one could only dream of just a few years ago.

Most of your favourite spirit drinks and liqueurs are available from your brew shops as essences with complete instructions on how to make your favourite spirit. The range is vast with many choices of the same type. As an example, there so many whiskies available that at least one of them will taste like your favoured beverage.

Top Shelf Cocktail Book - Ingredients

This section is a reprint from the Still Spirits book called Top Shelf Cocktail Book and is owned and marketed from New Zealand by Fermtech Wholesalers Ltd. It is Copyright © 1999 by Fermtech Wholesalers Ltd and has been reproduced with their permission. I recommend this book as a definitive guide to making all your spirits, liqueurs and cocktails because of their fantastic range of flavours available. Some of the flavours will make 1.125 Litre and others will make 5 Litre of spirit from just one 50ml of essence.

Alcohol

The resultant alcohol percentage of the liqueur depends of course on the volume and strength of the alcohol added. All the other ingredients have a watering down effect on the alcohol. This is why in the case of Italiano for instance we start of with 780mls of 50%/Volume Alcohol (/V) and end up with 1125mls at 35%/V. If you are purchasing ready made alcohol you will generally find that the most economical strength to purchase is about 37%/V. Some recipes suggest that you use 50%/V. If you use weaker alcohol the resultant liqueur will be correspondingly lower. This should not unduly concern you, as most liqueurs are very high in alcohol anyway. The only area where it will cause problems is if you wish to light the liqueur in the case of flaming Sambucas etc... As most stills produce alcohol above 50%/V you have more flexibility to make the liqueurs at the correct strength.

Cream

For cream liqueurs only. The ideal cream to use is UHT Longlife Lite. This will keep better than standard cream but all cream liqueurs should be drunk fresh and kept refrigerated. To extend the life of a cream liqueur, mix up all the ingredients except the cream and then add cream just prior to drinking. Lite cream will make a lighter liqueur and does not have the fat content of normal cream so it is less prone to spoiling.

Liquid Glucose

There are many different types of Liquid Glucose available. We recommend the Still Spirits Liquid Glucose as it has the correct thickness level and has virtually no sweetness. This is added purely to give the liqueur mouth feel and consistency. Stand in hot water before use.

Liqueur Thick

This is a dried form of Liquid Glucose. Still Spirits Liqueur Thick has been formulated to give the correct thickness level without adding any unwanted flavours while providing no extra sweetness. Powdered glucose or dextrose can not be substituted as this is a simple sugar which adds sweetness but very little thickness.

White Sugar

This is added to give sweetness to the liqueur. All measurements are in millilitres (ml) so no scales are necessary.

Water

Ordinary tap water is added to reach the correct alcohol content. If your water has a funny taste or it is not safe for drinking use filtered or distilled water.

Top Shelf Classic Range

Developed for those who want the very best.
This is a commercial quality essence.
Each sachet will flavour 2.25 Litres of filtered alcohol.

American Bourbon	Brandy Gin	Calypso Dark Rum
Navy Dark Rum	Queensland Dark Rum	Scotch Whisky
Tennessee Bourbon	Finest Reserve Scotch Whisky	

Top Shelf Spirit

A range developed for the connoisseur in mind.
Each 50 ml bottle will flavour 2.25 Litres of filtered alcohol.

Bourbon	Dark Rum	English Gin
French Brandy	Jamaican Dark Rum	Kentucky Bourbon Rye
Whisky	Scotch Whisky	Smoky Whisky
Rye Whiskey	White Rum	

Original

This is the most cost effective range of flavours.
Care has been given to select these essences for their widespread appeal. Each 50 ml bottle will flavour 5 Litres of filtered alcohol.

Blended Whisky	Bourbon	Brandy
Chilli Vodka	Citrus Vodka	Dark Rum
Gin	London Dry Gin	Tequila
Vodka	Whisky	White Rum

Spirit Additives - Top Shelf

To create those finishing touches.

Distillers Caramel	Distilling Conditioner	Glycerine
Mellow Oak		

Top Shelf Liqueur

All Top Shelf Liqueurs make one 1.125 Litre bottle.

Amaretto	Apricot Brandy	Banana Schnapps
Blackberry Schnapps	Black Sambuca	Blue Curacao
Butterscotch Cream	Butterscotch Schnapps	Cafelua
Cherry Brandy	Chocolate Mint	Coconut Rum
Coffee Cream	Coffee Maria	Cream de Cacao
Cream de Menthe	Dictine	Hazelnut
Irish Cream	Italiano	Macadamia Nut
Melon Liqueur	Orange Brandy	Peach Schnapps
Sambuca	Skybuie	Southern Smooth
Strawberry Schnapps	Triple Sec	Dry Vermouth
Mango	Parfait Amour	Rum Liqueur
Red Sambucca	Swiss Chocolate Almond	

Mixing Recommendations - Still Spirits

Still Spirits recommends that the best way to mix up the liqueurs is to boil any water, then add the sugar and liquid glucose and stir well. You will find it very helpful to first warm the liquid glucose by immersing in hot water or heating in the microwave. Add this to the alcohol and again warm the mix up to about 30° C and stir well. Once dissolved, cool the mix in the refrigerator. Once cool, the essence can be added; in the case of Cream Liqueurs, add cream.

The ranges of flavours listed in the last five headings are available from most brew shops that distribute Fermtech Wholesalers Ltd products and they are used to mix up around 120 other cocktail recipes listed in the Still Spirit Top Shelf Cocktail Book. It is beyond the scope of this Manual to list these recipes so I recommend that you purchase a copy of the Still Spirit Top Shelf Cocktail Book as your guide to mixing many cocktails.

Traditionally Aging your Spirit

The brew industries have traditionally aged their spirit in oak barrels for many years. Sometimes the spirit will reside inside barrels for ten years or more for some of the finest cognacs and brandies. These barrels are 300Ltr or more in some cases and lay resting in dark and gloomy cellars until ready for bottling. There seems to be some mystery that is not fully understood by scientists and chemists alike as to the amazing metamorphosis that takes place during the apparently dormant slumber years of the contents.

However, many years ago the thrifty Scottish whisky brewers used old reassembled oak casks that formally contained sherry and were then discarded. The distinctive taste of Scottish whisky was born. That was not the only reason for the exceptional taste, but did contribute to it. The old Kentucky Moonshiners would reassemble second hand barrels using a wood fire to aid bending the staves before reassembly. Sometimes a number of these staves would accidentally become charred during the heating process. Because they were also thrifty and trying to survive in an industry that was concealed from the excise collectors, the burnt staves were used in the assembly with an amazing discovery. The spirit from these barrels with burnt staves had a superior mellow flavour compared to that of the unburnt barrels. Now we had the birth of fine Kentucky Bourbon, and to this day the insides of these barrels are charred. Sound familiar to slowly filtering through activated carbon?

You can also take advantage of these well-known phenomena of aging your precious spirit in oak casks. A 300-litre cask may to a little large for the home brewer and distiller. Luckily a smaller cask of 4 through to 50 litres has a huge advantage for the home Moonshiner. The 300Ltr cask, although having a large inside surface area, does not present such a large surface area to the cubic volume contents as a smaller cask. A smaller 6Ltr cask has the ability to age and mellow its contents a lot faster than a mammoth sized cask.

We can take advantage of this smaller barrel phenomenon to continuously age our spirit and drinking some also at the same time. Any of your darker spirits, Whisky, Brandy and Rum can be aged in oak barrels using a specially developed method from the HokiNooki Moonshiners. We don't need to wait ten years to age our spirit before sampling, then finding that it tastes as if it was aged in an old sock or under garments, resulting in redistillation and filtering. This would be a bitter experience for the budding Moonshiner to learn that the efforts of the past 300Ltr barrel contents was appalling.

So how do we do it?

It has been said that all spirit stored in oak casks contain fusel oil and that this is part of the aroma of Brandy, Whisky, dark Rum etc. Excess fusel oil intensifies a possible hangover. Spirits blended from essences contain little or no fusel oil hence one is more likely to feel fine the next day, unless one has drunk too much. We will take advantage of both the essence and oak barrel theories to age and flavour our spirit.

You can make use of a second hand barrel if you are assured that the former contents were of the potable spirit or wine type. We don't want to use barrels that have contained vinegar or some type of motor spirit or poison during their past life.

Cleaning your Barrel

A 5% solution of soda ash can be used to clean the inside of your barrel by completely filling it with this mixture and soaking it for 24 hours. After which you will need to rinse it with a 5% mixture of citric acid to neutralise the alkaline soda ash. Now, completely fill your barrel with clean water and leave it for one week. Remember to fit the wooden or rubber stopper during this process. After this soaking, open the stopper and run your finger around the inside of the barrel. There should not be any slippery fungal coating on the inside. If there is you will need to take some drastic action. A further cleaning process of chlorine will be required. Dilute at the rate of one cup (225ml) of household bleach Sodium Hypochlorite (chlorine bleach) to 5Ltr of water and fill your barrel to the top. After 24 hours, rinse your barrel twice per day with clean water for one week. Then immediately fill your barrel with alcohol before it has a chance to attract any more bacteria. Sodium Metabisulphite or Sulphur Tablets may work well instead of chlorine, depending on the fungal growth. To save you all this cleaning carry on, buy one from your Brew Shop.

Fitting taps to your Barrel

The tap fitted to the bottom of your cask can be wooden or old-fashioned brass tank tap. Be careful that they don't leak. A better solution is a quarter turn ball valve that looks like a normal household tap. This tap will be able to thread directly into the woodenhead of your barrel. A good idea is to screw a $\frac{3}{4}$ to $\frac{1}{2}$ inch stainless or plastic reducer into the head of the barrel, then fit a $\frac{1}{2}$ inch tap into this reducer. This will allow you to change a troublesome tap without disturbing the wooden barrelhead. With a little patience you will be able to locate a good traditional looking tap for your barrel that will look fine residing on your bar. Don't forget to make a good looking gantry to perch your show piece on.

Filling and using the contents

Now that your reconditioned or new barrel is set up and ready for use, we need to fill it with spirit. Before preparing your barrel, you will need to accumulate your barrel size (4 or 50Ltr) of distilled and filtered spirit. A new barrel ought to be soaked with clean water by completely filling it and leaving it until all leaks have stopped. Your spirit must be at 50% alcohol. The barrel should be filled completely to the stopper. When filled, the stopper will need to be lightly tapped into place. The stopper will seal after swelling of the wood has taken place. Now leave your full barrel sitting on your bar for at least two months. This is the aging process that we talked about.

After two months have elapsed, you are ready to sample your long awaited, well-earned efforts. Let's consider that you're about to make some Rum. Follow the instructions in the section Making Spirits and Liqueurs on page 24, except when it comes to adding the measured quantity of spirit. The section that states that: "Now add the 832ml of 50% spirit" needs to be changed to "Now add 416ml of spirit from your barrel and 416ml of 50% clear filtered spirit". That is we have $\frac{1}{2}$ barrel spirit and $\frac{1}{2}$ normal spirits that has not been aged. The reason for this is because the essences take care of the aging taste to some extent. If you were to use only aged spirit, the taste would be too strong. The colour of your aged spirit will be an awesome golden shade that would challenge any connoisseur's opinion. As for the taste and aroma, the same will apply after a further 4 weeks aging in the bottle.

Now that you have taken some spirit from your cask, top it up again without delay, as it should be kept full and sealed at all times. Doing this will give you a continuous supply of golden aged spirit for making all your darker favourite alcoholic beverages.

As mentioned earlier, the essences have been produced with a complete and complex taste in mind without using spirit from a barrel. So one ought to do some experimenting with the amount of essence. You should be able to use approximately $\frac{1}{2}$ the recommended essence and get good results because you are adding the taste of the aged barrel spirit.

One rather cunning method of producing brandy without any essence is to distill some old rough unsaleable wine and age it in your cask. A few months later you may be surprised. Also experiment with filtering through activated carbon to produce a rough kind of cognac. But please remember that superb cognac is a product from good quality grapes.

The difference is in the Taste

It is no accident producing a cleaner, smoother, softer spirit with an individual flavour. It is simply the art of the individual distiller. The processes for success are easy if you follow some simple rules.

Clean fermentation

Spending a little extra money on good yeast produced for the manufacture of spirit is paramount along with pure clean sugars and contamination free clean water without chlorine. Rainwater is often used. Anything other than pure water is at a risk of producing a Wash alive with bacteria and an enormous array of distillable chemicals and alcohols like methylated spirit and fusel oils. All utensils and containers must be sterilised before and after use. Read the instructions published on the yeast pack for guidance.

Using white granular sugar at the rate of 250 to 300g per litre of water and a good balanced yeast nutrient will produce good fermentation with 16% alcohol. Dextrose used at 400g per litre will produce an extremely clean fermentation resulting in a Wash of around 20% alcohol with good yeast.

Low temperature Distillation

To become an experienced distiller will take time and expertise. It is an art with the single aim to take off ethanol leaving all else behind or discarded. If you are not using a Reflux Still then a Pot Still requires that a low controlled temperature be used, without boiling, during the entire distillation. A hard boiling system will produce a hard foul smelling spirit.

Don't be greedy

As a rule of thumb, one litre of 40% consumable spirit per one kilogram of sugar is a reasonable yield that you can expect. Trying for higher yields will run the risk of contaminated spirit with plenty of headaches. Go for quality, not quantity and you will live well to tell the tale.

Always treat with new Activated Carbon

There are many methods of treating your spirit with activated carbon. One basic thing to remember is that slower is better. Carbon is used for stripping out unwanted flavours, odours and colours to produce a clinically clean neutral spirit. Carbon is used at 10 to 25g per litre of spirit, stirred daily for one week then another week to settle. This is a minimum requirement. Or you can use the connoisseurs method described under Purification System on page 70 as it is far superior.

Mellowing and Oaking

A secret of the experienced distiller is the process of Oak Aging. The finest brandy, rum and whisky has always been aged in oak barrels taking up to ten years to produce the finest spirit and reputation. Some brandy has a reputation to be 100 years old from oak casks. The home distiller need not wait 100 years as tasting this may present a challenge.

The home distiller need not go to the expense of oak barrels to start with because they can achieve similar results with extremely good products available from a brew shop. They are Aging Syrup and American Oak Granules. Mellow Oak essence is one product that you can use and you are not aging many years before sampling your brew.

Follow the instructions, but be careful not to use too much as oak has a subtle softening effect rounding the spirit while adding taste and colour. Barrel Oak Granules are manufactured for both the home brewer and professional wine makers and distillers alike.

As a rule, you can expect this aging process to take from 14 days to 2 months, depending on the aging requirement of you spirit type. Rum is the fastest and Whisky is the slowest to age.

Finally is the Taste Test

Naturally the taste of your spirit will be the subject of ones likes and dislikes and is up for discussion. Many folks will like the harsh, sharp pungent flavour of old naval rum and primitive whisky. Others will be looking for the more subtle tastes of an old smoky single malt whisky.

To get you thinking about what to look for without all the often-trendy terminologies, here is a judging list to get you started.

We look for clean fresh odour with absents of foul oils often found in rough wine. A slightly sweet or pleasant after smell noticeable when both tasting and sniffing. The tongue will notice a melting feeling and warmth at the back of the throat. A grin from ear to ear will be the final determination. Your head will be clear the next morning if have not been too indulgent.

The absence of too much smoky flavours from burnt distillation. Fire like explosion burning your tongue and throat. Oily colourless flavour produced from fusel oils. Overpowering odour. Sharp and/or pungent old zoo or dog odours. Tears in the eyes from the fumes and blaspheming statements and swearing. Guidance of a superior being from above.

We strive for unique and pleasant flavours without headaches.

Making HokiNooki Moonshine

What is HokiNooki Moonshine?

HokiNooki Moonshine is a home brewed and distilled alcohol that is generally in the form of Whisky, Brandy, Rum or similar spirit. Making home brewed beer is legal in Australia, but at the time of writing, using a still for the manufacture of spirit is a federal offence due to health and excise tax issues. Hopefully this will change soon.

Making HokiNooki Moonshine

This process covers simple preparation of the Mash for fermentation and finally distillation. The first piece of advice given in a 1907 publication was to go to the woods and find a suitable clearing to hide your still. This is sincerely good advice in some countries.

You will require 30 kilograms of grain in the form of barley, wheat, rye or corn (maize), 30 kilogram of sugar, 170 litres of warm water. Wash your grain thoroughly. Bakers yeast will be used, so half a kilo will be sufficient. Also a huge plastic (food quality) bin for fermenting your Mash, as the fermenting vessel, will be required, probably in excess of 200 litres.

Fully dissolve the sugar with 30 litres, or more, of water heated to just under boiling point. Tip the rest of the warm water and grain into your bin and stir well. Let the mixture stand until the temperature cools to around 25°C. Mix up your yeast with some of the liquid Wash from your Mash and pitch it in to commence fermentation. Cover the concoction loosely with the lid to keep out all creepy crawlies. Remember that the gasses will build up pressure inside of your bin if completely sealed. This could cause an explosion and put itself into orbit. You could make up some sort of fermentation lock as previously described. Maybe a hose connected to the lid with the loose end dropped into a bucket of water will be required.

Leave this potion for 2 weeks to ferment. When fermentation ends, there will be a noticeable reduction of action inside the bin and no more bubbles. Now you can drain off the Wash through a fine mesh screen to remove any particles. Adding finings to settle the cloudiness could further clear the resulting liquid. Your final clear Wash is now ready for distillation.

If you don't clear your Wash, two things could happen during distillation. Firstly, foul smelling, headache producing fusel oils could be present in your precious spirit. Secondly, the steam line could become clogged causing the still to explode, probably taking your house and legs with it.

If the pressure becomes too great in a poorly designed still, the resulting explosion could leave a sizeable gap in the woods. No need for you to worry about the taxman calling because you will be able to see him nearing during your orbit around the Earth.

Be warned: unless the temperature stays between 70 and 91°C at the top of your still during distillation, the resulting grog will kill you. One slip up and its jail, hospital, or the morgue for you, my son.

Old Barley Maize HokiNooki Rum

Make up a concoction from 15 Kilos of cracked corn, 5 Kilos of kibbled malted barley, and 4 Kilos of malt syrup, 12 Kilos of dark molasses and half a kilo of bakers yeast. You could add some citrus fruit, skin and all, to complement the taste.

Remove the lid of a 200 Litre plastic drum and place the washes corn and barley inside. Fill the drum with warm water and stir vigorously. Chuck in the malt, molasses and mangled citrus, and stir well. When the mixture has cooled to around 25°C, pitch in the yeast, stir well again and pray.

As previously mentioned, allow fermenting completely for about 2 weeks before filtering off the liquid Wash. Allow settling before distilling. Follow the instructions under the heading *Making HokiNooki Moonshine* for fermentation and distilling and you should have fantastic Rum, especially if you were to age it in an old oak barrel for a while.

Old Barley Whisky

Firstly one must complete the *Making HokiNooki Moonshine* using barley for the grain. Barley is used for the traditional Scottish Whisky. So you could try toasting your barley over peat smoke to add to the flavour. Keep the grain moving when toasting because we don't want a fire in the 4-gallon toasting vessel.

Now mix 3.5 Litres of Moonshine with 2 cups of brown crystal sugar made from maple syrup. Add 2 cups of citrus, your choice of type, cut and not peeled. Load up some bottles and leave until settled. Siphon off the cleared spirit after a few weeks and taste. If all else fails, tip it down the drain and head down to the local bottle-o for some palatable grog.

Bourbon and Rye Whisky

This is simply a process of *Making HokiNooki Moonshine* using mainly corn (maize) for Bourbon and rye for Rye Whisky as your grain. Aging in an oak barrel, charred inside, to mellow it, is strongly recommended.

Traditional Whisky or Bourbon (Sugarless)

The term sugarless is not totally correct, except for the fact that you don't add sugar to your Mash. It is converted from the grain by malting. This will be a smaller brew compared with *HokiNooki Moonshine,* as this one needs a little more expertise for a successful spirit. There are several basic steps in making good grain wort. It may appear complex at first, but once learned, you will be able to master a price efficient method of producing a rather unique spirit that will amaze both you and your friends.

Cover 1 Kilo of barley with warm water at temperature 17 to 30° C for 24 hours. Change the water and soak for a further 24 hours. Skim off anything that floats like husks, broken grain and contaminants. Continue this process for up to one week ensuring that the barley is kept warm and mixed daily. This barley must not dry out. If it begins to sprout, discontinue the soaking process.

Spread the barley out over a wet surface. Wet towels or clean sacks will suffice if not allowed to dry out. Keeping the room temperature at 17 to 30° C will help germination. Turning the barley 3 times daily, and waiting until it sprouts. Sprouting may take from one week to ten days. The enzymes in the germinating barley are converting the starches into fermentable sugars. Now you can see where our sugar comes from.

When the shoots are between 6 to 8mm long, the sprouted barley needs to be dried out, preferably in a low temperature oven. During drying the malted barley, the temperature should not exceed 50° C at first, until the barley appears to be dried. This can take a number of hours. Now you can raise the temperature in 5° C steps, not to exceed 80° C. Keep the temperature constant for an hour or so during each step. The barley is now fully malted. As a guide for pale ale malt: Day 1, 32 to 38° C. Day 2, 38 to 49° C. Day 3, 60° C raising to 82° C at PM. Day 4, 77° C.

Another drying method is to spread the barley thinly, close to an open window or breeze so that it dries very slowly. This could take more than a week for completion. It must be turned at least twice per day.

If one were trying to mimic the Scottish method, you would quietly smoke the barley over smouldering peat. This may produce a single malt flavour if all goes well. Worth trying if you can locate some peat.

Cleaning and de-sprouting the malted barley is simply a process of placing the grain in a sack or pillowcase and beat it repeatably against a hard surface, a post will do. After all rootlets are broken loose, place the barley in a sieve and toss it into the air so that the rootlets and chaff will fall through the sieve holes. A small breeze or fan can be helpful.

Some brewers prefer to age their malt for at least a few months before use. One should experiment with this at later stage of experience.

Now is the interesting stage. Take your malted barley and grind it (kibble) using a course-grind grinder or coffee grinder. Even a rolling pin is useful for this purpose. This will be added to a warm cooked porridge made from 4 Kilo of kibbled clean unmalted grain of your choice and 20 Litre of clean water. Keep this concoction warm at 56 to 68° C until the porridge thins out noticeably, indicating that the thickened gelatinised grain starch has converted into a soluble sugar. Using this method has saved you the hassle of malting 5 Kilos of grain. The enzyme from your 1 Kilo of barley has converted the extra 4 Kilo into fermentable sugar. Now we have our fermentable sugar. Malted barley is also available from your brew shop.

When the Mash is below 22° C, strain the resulting liquid from the solids into your fermenting vessel adding up to 100g of yeast nutrient and 20g of high activity yeast. Top up with clean water to 23 Litres. If you are pedantic, add some citric acid to reduce the PH to 5.3. Fit the vessel lid and fermentation lock and keep the temperature between 20 to 25° C until fermentation is complete in about 3 to 5 days, maybe longer.

Decant the Wash from any sediment into your distillation pot ready for distillation. Your choice of a simple Pot Still and Reflux Still is a question of strength and flavour. The Pot Still will give you more of the grain flavours but care needs to be exercised so that Meths and Fusel Oils are discarded. Normally the Jocks will process their Wash using a Pot Still into their low wine receiver. This will give them a 15 to 30% spirit. Then again using a Pot Still for the final distillation to produce 50% spirit for their oak barrels. The Reflux Still will give you the 50% strength spirit in one distillation and the flavours from the grain are quite noticeable. The advantage of a Reflux Still is that the Meths and Fusel's are more controllable and a cleaner spirit will result, not to mention your lower power bill. Now your well-earned spirit can be stored in charred oak barrels for at least 3 months or you can use prepared toasted oak chips for the same purpose. Either way will mellow, add colour and flavour during aging.

Now for the question of whether we brewed Whisky, Bourbon or Rye Whisky. One needs to use malted (1Kilo) barley for any of the aforementioned. The balance is important. Whisky requires Barley. Bourbon requires Corn (maize). Rye requires Rye grain. Greater than 51% of this grain type is important for the final spirit to be authentic. So 4Kilo is well within limits.

Now you are really making true HokiNooki Moonshine.

Wine and Beer Distillation - Be Careful

Wine and beer distillation comes under the category of Moonshine because it is one process that is not fully defined in terms of quality. It is the process by which we grab hold of as much off beer or rotten wine that we can lay our hands on. It is processed to such an extent that we end up with pure alcohol as previously discussed. So how do we do it?

One problem that we will encounter is the quality issue. We should assume that there is plenty of methanol and fusel oils. We are required to remove all the nasties to uphold our standards that we adhere to. So we will assume the worst-case scenario at all times.

The apparatus that will be required are two stills. One to reduce the size of the raw material, then one to purify the results from the first still.

Assume that we have 100 litres of beer that cannot be consumed even by the most avid drinkers. Locked up in that quantity we have 5 litres of pure alcohol at 100%. That is assuming that the beer is currently at 5% alcohol content.

Firstly we load the beer into a still pot, of rather large size, with a Pot Still condenser attached to the top. By the way, we can have multiple sessions of this distillation in a smaller boiling vessel. We use a Pot Still for this process to reduce the size of the total bulk at a faster speed than the Reflux Still is capable of.

Once we are all set up and ready to run, apply the heat source and keep an eye on the temperature of the distillate. Once starting to flow, we will discard anything under 75° C because that will be associated to methyl alcohol. Remember our quality system. Now we collect everything that flows above 75° C because this will probably be worth keeping. All that emerges from the Pot Still must be filtered through a coffee filter paper because there may be a large fusel oils content appearing. Now we break the rules for a short time. Collect all that emerges from the Pot Still until the temperature of the Pot Still has reached 93° C. We collect all the output until just below the boiling point of water at 100° C. Now we have reduced our original 100 litres down to around 20 litres. Now it is a manageable quantity for the Reflux Still. Maybe now some of you will understand why we mount a thermometer in the top of a Pot Still system.

With your collection of around 20 litres, we must proceed to the next stage of distillation, and that is fractional distillation using a Reflux Still, possibly more than once. Because of the potential nasty components of our distillate, we must be careful with this next stage of purification.

Pour the results of the Pot Still into the boiling vessel of your Reflux Still. Again we apply the heat to the boiling vessel. But this time we watch the temperature like a hawk. As the temperature rises, we watch for 65° C, as this is the methanol temperature that could appear as spirit from your Reflux Still. We discard anything under the temperature of 75° C because of the risks involved in an unknown brew. Now we collect all that emerges from the Reflux Still until 91° C, because above this we may get some headache material of fusel oils. At any case we must stop collection of spirit below 40% alcohol content because of impurities. By now you will have more or less 10 litres of 50% spirit.

Normally, at this stage, we must sniff the resulting distillate to ascertain the purity and odour of our collection. A taste would also help. Sometimes if the quality is so bad, we must redistill this distillate again, this time diluting it with the same quantity of pure water.

Now that you have a high quality and pure distillate, it must be diluted to 50% alcohol content, and then filtered through activated carbon. Sounds familiar? To use anything else less than the quality of the filter described in section Purification System on page 70 would be doubtful as to the excellence of your spirit. Remember that we are not trying to produce Brandy or Whisky at this stage as we are attempting to recover the pure alcohol from reject wine or beer. Also we must not loose sight of the quality of the original beer or wine, because it was a little rough, and that is why we are processing it.

Wine needs a little extra care in many cases. Sometimes you may be able to get hold of expired white wine or reject red wine. Both of these wines rely on fusel oils to enhance their tastes. Be extra cautious to adhere to the above distillation and filtering procedures to get a pure alcohol product. It must be remembered that distilled grape wine is the only alcohol that is desired for the fortification of wines into Port. So use this distillate to produce some rather nice Port for your own consumption.

Another point that you may want to look at is the distillation of grape wine to produce a homemade Brandy. After distillation you can pour the distillate into an oak cask and let it age for a few years. Maybe you will end up with a superior Brandy or Cognac. We live in hope!

This section is not to encourage the new budding spirit maker into ventures beyond their capability. It is by way of encouragement for future endeavours that will prove interesting and challenging.

You never know when someone will donate 200 litres of rough wine for you to experiment with. But be careful with the quality issues.

Understanding Fermentation

To produce good spirits and liqueurs there is no need to understand the science of fermentation. If you want to experiment with fermentation, then reading this section will help uncover some of the mysteries, else you may skip this subject until later when you have become more experienced.

Seeing fermentation from the yeast's perspective will help you get a better understanding of this process. Nature has many types of fermentation, but the only one of interest to the brewer is yeast and sugar fermentation to produce ethanol. Yeast is a very small living organism similar to the cells in the human body. Many folks think of yeast as just another ingredient similar to sugar to produce alcohol. Nothing could be further from the truth.

Just as other biological cells, yeast has one major goal in life, to reproduce. To achieve this end, it produces daughter cells as buds, similar to the parent cell. With a plentiful supply of sugar, minerals, amino acids and oxygen and the correct temperature it will reproduce itself every 30 minutes. If this were to continue, you would soon end up with a huge amount of yeast cells. Remove the oxygen and there will be much less growth and you will finish up with alcohol and CO_2. As far as yeast is concerned, sugar is a great source of energy. It gobbles it up at an alarming rate. Glucose has 6 carbon atoms connected by chemical bonds. These bonds get broken down one by one, liberating energy during the process. If there was no oxygen present, then it will only break one bond with far less energy, so there will be less growth. Waste products will be generated in the form of ethanol and CO_2. This is why we must exclude oxygen by keeping it out of the fermentation vessel.

Fermentation of $C_6H_{12}O_6$ Produces $2\ C_2H_5OH\ +\ 2\ CO_2$

Fermentation of Sugar Produces 2 x Ethanol plus 2 x Carbon Dioxide.

For yeast to grow, it also requires amino acids, enzymes and minerals along with extracts from sugar. Apart from the sugar, we group the others into Yeast Nutrients. They include di-Ammonium phosphate and magnesium sulphate to actively reduce fusel oil production. Potassium, phosphate, nitrogen, calcium and niacin are required for growth and cell structure. Without these nutrients, fermentation will fail very soon because it will be unable to tolerate the increasing level of alcohol.

Good turbo yeast will contain all of these essential growth ingredients collectively known as yeast nutrients. Trying to ferment sugars and yeasts without nutrients will yield very little alcohol.

Fermentation Temperature

We need to watch both the surrounding air and the Wash liquid temperature during fermentation. The liquid temperature will normally be higher than the air temperature and this difference will soar as the volume increases. Elevated temperatures are fatal for yeast fermentation.

With the absents of alcohol, yeast will be arrested above 40°C, but unfortunately, alcohol increases the fatally. At 13 to 15% alcohol, which is easily achieved, the death temperature drops to the low 30s °C and 20% alcohol is down to mid 20s °C. With a 25Ltr brew, the temperature differential between the liquid and ambient air is only a few degrees, so fermentation is easy to accomplish. But with a larger brew of 200Ltr you will need to introduce some frozen plastic bottles of water to lower the temperature below 30°C. The 1st 12 hours are critical. Imagine what happens in the tropics! Many brewers wait till winter to help with this challenge. Some newer Turbo yeasts are tolerant of higher temperatures.

There is another reason to keep the temperature down below 30°C, that is, to reduce the production of the unwanted fusel oils down to a minimum. Achieving a low temperature below 18°C is pushing things to far. It will exceed 2 weeks for the completion of fermentation. Often 18 to 25°C are ideal for most yeasts. If in doubt, read the instructions on the yeast sachet from your brew shop.

Temperature control, and more importantly, temperature stability are critical to ensure the quality of your brew. Constant temperatures are important and easily achieved during winter months with heat pads or brew belts. Often a Pet Pad or low wattage waterbed heater with its thermostat can be wrapped around your fermentation container with some carpet underlay. Summer months are a definite challenge. Opening the brew is risky but sometimes necessary to drop in some plastic iced water containers to reduce heat. The only problem here is that constantly held temperatures are impossible let alone the oxygen and other nasties that enter the brew container to infect it.

Water

Water is of concern to all brewers as it may contain many unwanted elements such as chlorine that was added by the municipal water supplies. Some brewers filter their water through activated carbon before brewing, some use bottled water, others carefully analyse their water. For most brewers, tap water is fine. But you may want to filter it then let it settle overnight, or even boil it to force out the chlorine additives.

Minerals and Ions in the water can be of interest, as Ions change the acidity of the Wash or Mash being fermented. An ideal acidity level is around 5.3 to 5.5 pH. Brewers often change their water's mineral composition by adding gypsum (Calcium Sulphate $CaSO_4$) or chalk (Calcium Carbonate $CaCO_3$). Sometimes Epsom salts will be used. They tell me that it gives you a good run for your money!

Many of the famous brewing locations around the world have a reputation for their techniques based upon individuality imparted by the local water supply. In England, Burton is a fine example. Their city's water is so hard that it imparts a sharp flavour that enhances the perception of bitterness in their fine ales.

Many brewing recipes instruct you to add ingredients such as salt and other water modifiers. Changing the characteristics of the water should be done with caution without consideration of your own tap water makeup.

Yeast

Generally, when brewing Wash for distillation, you have little choice of quality yeast. There are many first-rate Turbo Yeasts out there ready to use, available from brew shops. These normally do not require extra yeast nutrients to be added. However, for you beer brewers out there, a little knowledge will not go astray.

Ale yeast (*Saccharomyces cerevia*) ferments properly at temperatures of 14 to 21° C whereas the larger yeast (*Saccharomyces uvarum*) requires from 7 to 10° C for optimum performance. An enormous number of strains of these two basic types are available from brew shops as are the Turbo Yeasts for distillation purposes. The fermentation temperatures for Turbo Yeasts are generally noted on the package.

You can encourage yeast activity as a result of aerating the chilled wash by shaking it to introduce air, or sometimes through pumping air or oxygen through the Wash in the fermenter before pitching in the yeast.

Fermentation Infections

Infections are easy to keep under control with cleanliness and hygiene of all your utensils and equipment, even your tables or benches. Sterophos or Sodium Metabisulphite is normally used for this purpose. With care, a weak solution of Chlorine bleach is often used. Chlorine kills yeast; so rinse all your gear before commencement of fermentation.

An Aceto bacterium is the one that turns everything to vinegar - bad taste. *Ropey Bacteria* turns the brew into paste. Not a pretty sight - it is dead.

Sterilization of your Fermentation Vessel

The most important piece of equipment that requires sterilization is the Fermentation Vessel, so therefore requires a special page dedicated to the subject.

Firstly, before purchasing a new vessel, make sure that it manufactured from food quality (for potable use) material plastic, or stainless steel. Most folks prefer a translucent white plastic so that they can view the contents within. The lid must be wide enough, and easily removable, so that it can be easily cleaned before and after fermentation. It must have an adequate sealing method so as to exclude any outside air from entering. There must be a rubber grommet fitted in the top for the mounting of a reliable bubble trap. The inside and outside texture should smooth to the touch to allow cleaning without any ingrained dirty material to remain attached to the surface. A temperature sensitive strip type of stick on thermometer, with a range from 16 to 32 Deg C, should be fitted to the outside for monitoring the internal temperature.

When cleaning your Fermentation Vessel, **do not use any material that will scratch the surface**. Pot scrubs are definitely out. Scratches on the surface will allow bacteria to enter into the scoured surface, and remain there, awaiting the sugar and water mix for their food. This is where the unwanted fermentation will be able to commence and produce a foul brew. Before using this vessel for fermentation, it must be cleaned with household detergent and hot water. The detergent will remove any oily deposits from the surface. The next stage of cleaning is optional. Any stubborn stains can be removed using 50gr of Sodium Metasilicate (brews detergent) mixed with 5 litre of water. **Sterilising:** Many different types of sterilising chemicals can be used, but **Sodium Metabisulphite**, 50gr to 5 litre of water, is by far the most important as far as killing unwanted bugs is concerned. Sterophos (pink stain remover) and Chlorine are also suitable for this purpose, but not as efficient. All traces of these chemicals must be removed by rinsing with cold water several times before use commences. Sound familiar? Maybe it sounds like a repeat of a previous paragraph. Good, you must have paid attention at that time. Let it sink in to your brain structure because this is the most of all vessels to be sterilized. Remember to sterilize the lid, lid seal and tap mounted to this vessel also.

After rinsing, attach the lid, to seal the fermentation vessel, to prevent any contamination from entering. It is worth a mention in this section that you must add the yeast to your Wash as soon as possible to inhibit any wild bugs and unwanted yeasts starting premature fermentation.

Distillation Discussion

Distillation is a process when one will heat up the Wash, or a mixture of compounds, to boiling point and cool the steam back to a liquid, evaporation then condensation. A typical example of this is seawater, which contains a mixture of pure water and salts, along with many minerals. These dissolved solids will not evaporate to any appreciable extent in normal atmospheric conditions of sunlight and wind. But the water will. Hence the wind and heat of the sun on the oceans vaporises a mammoth amount of pure water, excluding almost all of the mentioned solids. This vapour can travel overland to combine with cool air that condenses them back into a liquid state that we call rain. Rainwater is considered by most to be pure water. So this relatively pure water is distilled from seawater in this manner.

Many mixtures of liquids with different boiling points can also be separated using this principle. During the rise in temperature of the mixture, one will begin to evaporate (alcohol at 78.3°) before another (water at 100°), causing separation in the original blend of homogenous mixture. This vapour will contain more of the liquid with the lowest boiling point that was in the original blend of solution. The separation of these liquids with differing boiling points will not accomplish the same degree of purity as was cited with solids and rainwater from seawater. In the case of a compound solution of liquids, the degree of separation will depend largely upon how far apart the boiling point of each separate element is in the original mixture. The concentration and nature of each component will also have an effect on the recovery. Nevertheless, the separation can be known as a process of distillation. By this means alcohol is separated from the Wash solution of liquids and some solids.

The highest possible alcohol percentage that one can achieve by distillation is 95% because this mixture of alcohol and 5% of water has a lower boiling point of 78.15°, compared to that of 100% alcohol (78.3°). This is called an azeotrope. There's that word again.

Redistillation

Normally only one distillation will be required if care is taken with temperature using a Reflux Still. Sometimes you may want to distill some old wine or beer. If one wishes to distill twice, you can firstly distill once quickly through a simple Pot Still. Throw away the 1st 50ml fore shots. Then dilute the resulting distillate to 50% water and redistil slowly and accurately at 78° using a Reflux Still. This alcohol should then be reduced in percentage to 50% by adding pure water, or preferably to 38 to 42%, and then filtered through activated carbon. (50% is tolerable.)

This gives a tremendous result and the first distillation is accomplished very quickly. Before the second distillation one should Wash out the boiling vessel and still with the utmost care using a good wine cleaning agent or similar. Review Sterilising Your Equipment on page 14.

Extra Pure alcohol at 95%

Firstly one must distill the 25Ltr crystal clear Wash carefully once or twice throwing away the fore shots, which are the 1st 50ml. Keep the still temperature as low as possible so that distillate drops very slowly. Take away the rest (tails), when the alcohol percentage drops below 80%, for future redistillation. Always discard anything less than 40%. Now you will have distillate that will be in excess of 80%

Dilute the resultant distillate to 40% alcohol with pure water and filter through activated carbon. Carefully clean your boiling vessel with wine makers cleansing solution such as Sodium Metasilicate and rinse thoroughly. The Still can be cleaned with normal household detergent and water. Now redistil this filtered alcohol again using a Reflux Still. Throw away the 1st 20ml fore shots and collect 2 litres of approx 95%, more if turbo yeast was used. Stop collection if the percentage drops below 95%. This may take quite a few hours. The rest of the distillate can be used for future distillation.

You now have 95% alcohol that is extremely pure, which has already been filtered.

Methods of Proof Measurements

Distillations of potable beverages are normally measured in Proof. Proof varies in the method of measurement in USA, Canada, UK and possibly other countries. However, they are closely related with a little understanding. For simplicity we use the USA method, which is simply a method of twice the percentage by volume that was measured using your alcometer. So if your beverage contains 43% alcohol by volume, it is 86 Proof. It would appear that 51% alcohol by volume is termed as over Proof. Just to complicate things for you, let us consider 50% alcohol by volume in three different countries. In USA we would have 100 Proof, British would have it as 87.5 Proof Sykes and the Canadians would term that as -12.5 Proof. The Canadian system is actually closely related to the British system. If you are curious about this, look at the Tables and Reference section, Proof Table for Alcohol on page 88.

Fractional Distillation

The lower the temperature and the slower one distils the Wash, the more pure will be the alcohol. Fractional distillation is a tall column that extends vertically upwards from the boiling vessel. This column is similar in many respects to the large ones that you see distilling petrol and motor oil, except the petroleum distillation towers are designed to extract many different fractions concurrently.

The home distillation column has only one thing in mind, extracting ethyl alcohol from your Wash. We call this a Reflux Still. The length of the home Reflux Still extends from 300 to 600mm from the boiling vessel. This column is often filled with glazed ceramic pieces or glass marbles. These increase the surface area inside of the column and promote condensation at differing temperatures up the total length. The vapour passes upwards through the column until it has cooled down to liquid alcohol. Because of the differing boiling points of water and alcohol, a separation of these liquids occurs in the reflux column. This is termed fractionation, hence the term fractional distillation. The base of the column has a similar temperature to that of the boiling vessel, greater than the boiling point of alcohol, and the temperature at the top should be 78° C regulated by the heat source. So from the bottom to the top, the temperature falls off, all the way up. This causes the Wash water component with a higher boiling point to condense and run back down, into the boiling vessel. The alcohol travels all the way up without condensing until reaching the condenser section, which is over-the-top of the column, which is condensed back into a liquid. One can further improve the efficiency of the column by fitting two to three thin tubes horizontally through it. Check out Reflux Still Column on page 62. Cold water will pass via these tubes to cool down the column filling of ceramic or glass. By selecting to use one, two or three of these tubes, one can tailor the amount of cooling desired in the column. In this way we can get away from having a tall column that will require a large amount of heat. This through cooling separates water and fusel oil extremely efficiently by faster condensation. Regulation of the flow and temperature of the cooling water will regulate the temperature at the top of the column. Now one can set the heat source roughly, and fine tune with precision using the flow of cooling water to set the temperature at the top of the column.

Distillation results are far superior with the temperature set just under the boiling point of alcohol (78.319). Alcohol and water mix of 95% is 78.15° C, and is below the boiling point of 100% alcohol, a phenomenon known an azeotrope. This is an ideal temperature for excellent results to achieve the most pure alcohol.

Temperature Boundaries within a Reflux Column

If you were able to insert eight thermometers into you reflux column, you could possible realise these three scenarios. Each of the three columns of figures represents what could happen in the distillation column when the alcohol decreases in percentage in the boiling vessel as distillation progresses. We start distillation at 10% alcohol and finish with 0.5%.

Temperature °C and associated alcohol percentage inside the Column.

Start of Distillation		Middle of Distillation		Nearing End of Distillation	
78.15°	95%	78.15°	95%	78.15°	95%
78.15°	95%	78.15°	95%	78.50°	94%
78.15°	95%	78.50°	94%	79.00°	93%
78.50°	94%	79.00°	93%	79.50°	91%
79.00°	93%	79.50°	91%	81.00°	85%
79.50°	91%	81.00°	85%	82.00°	75%
81.00°	85%	82.00°	75%	90.00°	20%
82.00°	75%	90.00°	20%	94.00°	10%
Wash at 10%		**Wash at 2%**		**Wash at 0.5%**	
Vapour at 95° C		Vapour at 98° C		Vapour at 99° C	

These boundaries are not equidistant up the reflux column and are shown as eight possible sections that are simplified for graphical clarity. In reality these positions do not have defined measurable boundaries and the spacing between the lower ones are quite a lot larger than the higher sections which are actually quite small.

If you were to raise the temperature just a little to speed up the process of distillation, the top few sections would be popped out the top of the still column resulting in a weaker, more impure spirit. So hopefully, this will emphasise the importance of keeping the temperature accurate. If the temperature is held accurately, the threshold boundaries will be kept in place. You may even experience that the spirit will slow down, or stop, near the exhaustion of the alcohol from within the Wash. Even though the alcohol has stopped exiting, the still column has not actually stopped working. There is however, a large amount of activity inside the column because the whole system has created an equilibrium causing a rainstorm from within, keeping the temperature of the boiling vessel within safe limits. It should not boil dry because cooling is taking place from within the reflux column, down into the boiling vessel, then back up again.

Heat Source Discussion

Although we mentioned earlier that the safest heat source was electrical power, it is not so easy to control the heat without special equipment. Gas heat source has the advantage of infinitely variable flame within limits. It's, just a matter of choosing a suitable gas burner to suit your boiling vessel. The major disadvantage is that alcohol is highly flammable and one slip up with spillage, and not contained, your house is history.

If one uses an electrical hot plate or an electrical urn for a boiling vessel, usually there will be a device called a Simmerstat or thermostat to control the heat. Both of these devices will cycle on and off according to where you adjust the rotary dial. The temperature differential will usually be around 2 to 5 degrees. This cycling will cause surging of the temperature within your boiling vessel and surge boiling will not allow you to control the temperature of your distillation column to any degree of accuracy. So what is the answer?

One answer is to purchase a specially designed boiling vessel with an integral-heating element. This is fine except that if the power supply voltage was to vary from original design criteria, your boiling vessel and still combination may not be able to handle the changes in power fluctuations. As an example, a boiling vessel designed in New Zealand (230 volts) with an element of 1000 watts, would not be the same wattage in Australia because the power supply voltage is 240 volts. It would actually produce 1089 watts in Australia. But that is not the complete story. The power supply voltage varies within 10% of the stated voltage in each country. So this means that the minimum voltage in one country is 207 volts and the maximum in the other country is 264 volts. The resulting wattage variation is from 810 watts to a maximum of 1318 watts. This variation is intolerable for accurate distillation. This is possibly an economical solution that will work in most instances if the mains voltage is reasonably stable at 230 volts.

A better solution is to have an element, either integral or external, of a higher wattage than required. The heating element is connected to the power supply via a Triac type of power regulator. This type of vernier power regulator is often used for controlling the speed of hand drills and is similar to a high wattage light dimmer. It gives a continuously variable control of the heat or power, and the element can be set on maximum heat during the initial heating up stage. When the column is hot about half way up, the control knob can be set to reduce the heat to the required wattage. Before purchasing a Triac power regulator, make sure that it can handle the maximum wattage of your heating element capacity.

The next stage in sophistication can be achieved with a fully automatic type of electronic heat regulation. These can be broken down into two basic types. Both of them will use some type of electronic sensor in the top of the reflux column and will be controlled using low voltage for safety.

- Type one uses two heating elements; a Triac controller controls both. The second element can be of lower wattage if desired. An electronic temperature sensor will be placed in the top of the column. The sensor is hooked up to an electronic temperature controller. The second element is switched on and off via this controller. You can set the wattage of the primary element via the Triac controller so that it is slightly too low. The second element can be adjusted via its Triac controller to raise the temperature again. The distillation continues on the primary element during the "Too Hot" cycle and on both elements during the "Too Cold" cycle. Both elements set to full wattage will be used to raise the initial temperature of the boiling vessel.

- Type two uses only one heating element, larger than normally required. There is no Triac controller necessary but could be an advantage during initial heating of the boiling vessel. An electronic heat sensor will be mounted at the top of the reflux column and connected to a special electronic controller. The controller is known as a Proportional Integral Derivative (PID) controller. It predicts the rising temperature and slowly reduces the power delivered to the heating element. These controllers are used for very precise temperature controlling of scientific equipment. They often display the temperature down to more than two decimal places. To get technical about this controller, as the temperature is approached, the controller cycles on and off the power supply. By this method, the element will slow down as the temperature is reached and will not over-shoot the mark. Perfect temperature control can be realised using this type of electronic controller.

The disadvantage of these sophisticated hi-tech controllers is that one may loose contact with reality. Many brewers and distillers alike prefer to keep it simple and have some fun watching and adjusting water flow etc.

Limited cooling water, and a low wattage-heating source, could lead to changes in temperature from drafts through an open door. If this is so, increase both the heat and cooling water slightly until distillation becomes more stable at the same column head temperature. Keeping your apparatus insulated is also beneficial. You could wrap up your still pot with carpet underlay or a similar heatproof blanket. This would also save on heating costs. Be careful when using gas heating.

Triac Heat Controller Circuit Diagram

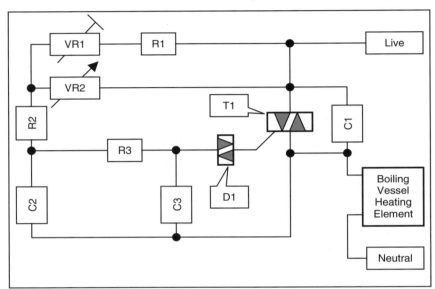

This Triac heat controller should not be constructed by anyone who does not have a background in electronics or electrical trades as dangerous mains voltages are present and can cause severe electric shock. This is a schematic diagram only that does not show the constructional details. Your knowledgeable electronics personnel will have the qualifications to assemble this controller with the appropriate precautions to save electrical hazards and electrocuting you. The constructional details have been omitted for obvious reasons.

Parts List

T1	Triac BTB 16-400	R1	470K 0.25W
D1	Diac BR 100-03	R2	18K 0.25W
C1	0.033uf 250 VAC	R3	10K 0.25W
C2	0.082uF 100 V	VR1	500K Preset Trim Pot
C3	0.047uF 50 V	VR2	500K Controller Pot

Your electronics expert will advise how easy this controller is to construct, as it resembles the circuit diagram of a light dimmer, except the Triac is much larger and dependant on the heating element size of your boiling vessel. The Triac should have an adequate heat sink to handle the power dissipation, and whole construction needs to be double insulated.

VR1 is preset so that there is always a minimum amount of heat.

Twin Heat Triac Controller Modification

This modification to the Triac Heat Controller Circuit Diagram on page 50 will enable you to use a single electric heat source with dual heat/wattage controllers. In operation, it will heat up the Wash to 78° at a high setting, and then automatically reduce the power when reaching that temperature. The actual low voltage controller is not shown in this diagram.

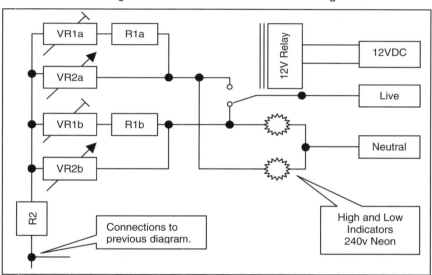

A low voltage temperature probe is inserted into the top of the Reflux Column and connected to a temperature controller. This temperature controller is set to 78° C and is connected to the *Relay* shown in this diagram. VR2a is adjusted so that it heats up the boiling vessel. When the temperature is reached, VR2b is adjusted so that it just maintains that temperature or slightly lower. In this way the temperature will cycle the *High and Low Indicator Lights* alternately, maintaining the correct temperature. VR2a can be set on full power during initial heating of the boiling vessel, and then backed off to be just a little too high.

If you use a sensitive and accurate temperature controller, this modification to the circuit on page 50 will perform close to the Proportional Integral Derivative (PID) controller described on page 49.

The values of VR1a-b, VR2a-b, and R1a-b are listed on page 50. R2 is the common entry connection point of both circuit diagrams.

Proportional Integral Derivative Heat Controller

This (PID) controller has some remarkable and expensive features. If price is not of concern, then this is the ultimate system to control the heat of your Reflux Still column.

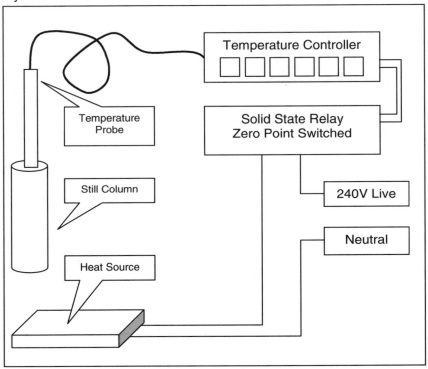

Parts List: Farnell Part #

Temperature Probe   Labfacility PT4 6 x 150   560-170

Temperature Controller   Omron E5C5-Q1PX   177-064

Solid State Relay   Crydom TDA2425   331-466

Turn to page 49 to review the advantages of using this type of sophisticated temperature controller. It is not intended for those who treat Home Brewing as a hobby because of the costs involved.

Qualified personnel should perform the construction. Part numbers chosen are suitable for 110v AC and 240v AC at 16 amps.

As a matter of Stills

There is a tremendous variety to the designs of stills capable of distilling a mixture of alcohol and water. You probably have seen or heard about many systems including laundry coppers, zip water heaters, pressure cookers and hot water urns. These could be coupled to a car radiator or an ingenious array of copper tube coils or serpentines. Nevertheless, the still can be an efficient and safe apparatus capable of producing clean potable spirit without too many hangovers. To accomplish these criteria, one must consider a few basic rules.

- Heating of the pot must be carefully controlled and monitored during the whole process of distillation. On no account should the Wash be boiled at 100° C at any time.

- The pot should have a large Wash surface area to promote circulation and vaporisation during heating. A short or squat pot is typical.

- The condenser should produce cool alcohol to stop it disappearing into the atmosphere. Lighter fractions can and should be discarded by monitoring the temperature at the still head.

- Stainless steel and copper are normally used for the construction of Stills. Stainless steel is easy to keep clean and will always look in showroom condition. Copper is the preferred material used in most Scottish whisky Stills.

- Ease of dismantling for cleaning before and after distillation.

- A good seal between the pot and still head as well as the lid.

Simple Still (Pot Still)

The term 'Pot Still' is often given to a simple still that has a pot for heating the Wash and a condenser connected to the top. You can conceive this in your mind as a Pressure Cooker as the pot, and the condenser would resemble some concoction of tubing connected to the top where the steam valve weight should be. The safety valve should be kept in tact. The pot would possibly sit on your kitchen range for the heat source. This is typical of the simplest system in existence today and days gone by.

This type of still is rather sloppy in its work. As is well known, water does evaporate without any heat supply. Obviously it evaporates even faster when heated. So during the extraction of your precious ethanol, a fair amount of water is collected at the same time. This results in a mixture of ethanol and too much water in the distillate. If the temperature is carefully controlled you will end up with more ethanol than water. So they do work satisfactorily with some extra care and attention.

The major disadvantage of this type of still system is that the purity of the spirit could be a little doubtful if you were to perform only one distillation. The only cure for this is to run the resulting distillate through your simple still again and again. Each time your ethanol will become more pure and in higher concentration compared with the water content. With care, two times through this still will suffice.

The cost of this type of simple still is low, but it is not very efficient in terms of heating cost and labour for the home distiller. All this said and considered one must remember that most of ye old Scottish Whisky stills are of this type, but of a larger scale and often fine tuned with a hammer!

Pot Still Drawing

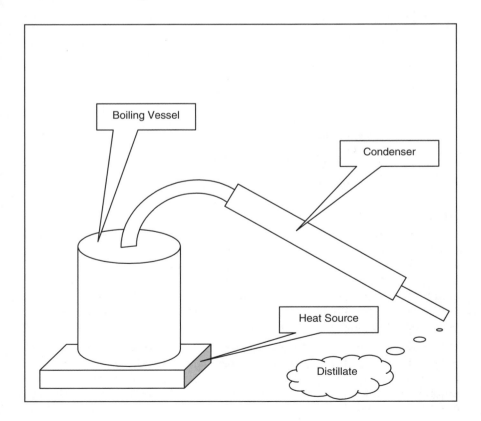

Reflux Still

Most distillers of home spirits today use Reflux Stills because of their rather unique design permitting a single distillation to achieve pure alcohol. These stills create a pre condensation area where the heavier fractions are returned back to the pot. The lighter alcohols are separated, as they are in a fractional distillation system similar to the principle used for petrol and motor oil. The Reflux unit is simply a small fractional distillation column with only one purpose. That is to produce pure ethyl alcohol.

The tower is packed with glass marbles or glazed ceramic material that offers a large surface area for the earlier stages of condensation. Naturally the cooler marbles are towards the top and most condensation will occur there. As the temperature decreases up the column, only the lighter fractions continue upwards towards the actual condenser. The heavier fractions pour back down the tower eventually into the Wash again. This action has a major side benefit, a stabilising effect on the Wash temperature resulting in less heat control required.

Of course, some ethanol also condenses out on the cooler top marbles. But as the liquid descends back down the column, the hotter marbles tend to evaporate the ethanol, so that it will proceed back up again. Inverse or Reflux action has taken place. The vapour travelling upwards tends to become more pure ethanol with this Reflux action.

By setting the temperature at the top of the column accurately, only the alcohols, with little water, will be selectively extracted during one distillation session. The resulting distillate will produce cleaner and higher strength spirit. The fusel oils will be left behind in the still pot.

A single run through a simple Pot Still will yield distillate containing 20 to 40 percent ethanol. That is as opposed up to 90 percent with a single run through a Reflux Still with the same Wash concentrations.

Temperature stabilisation is far easier realised using a Reflux Still. When set correctly, it will require far less attention throughout the complete distillation process. The still can sometimes slow down from a flow to a drip then ceases completely if the temperature is correctly and skilfully adjusted and the alcohol nears exhaustion. The Reflux column actually creates an artificial rainstorm that circulates from within the complete still pot and column. This action keeps the Wash from reaching the boiling point of water and produces a far more pure spirit.

Most serious home distillers will finish up with a Reflux Still. It will be worth the extra expense for fewer hangovers.

Reflux Column Filling

Here we discuss the virtues of a variety of Reflux Still column fillings. The packed column, which will be mounted above the boiling vessel, has only a limited capacity to allow vapours to rise up through the filling against the downward flow of condensed liquid, so the boil-up rate must not be too great, or the column will choke.

A perfect column filling ought to be 5 to 8mm in size, have a large surface area and be smooth, glazed or polished glass, in order to impart a quick and uninterrupted runback. Glass spheres like marbles are generally too large to give perfect fractionation in the column. The major advantage of marbles is the ease of purchase and they work quite well and they are easily cleaned. There are many stills using marbles successfully. There are not many major disadvantages using glass marbles unless one wants to be pedantic.

The column filling is a once only cost, so if you are a perfectionist, we can look at another solution. Raschig rings of glazed porcelain are reputed to be the answer. They resemble small pieces of cut tube and have a far superior surface area compared to marbles, about 3 times the surface area for the same size. They are widely used as boiling stones for distributing heat in a boiling vessel in both the chemical and brewing industries. A supplier of these may be difficult to locate in most countries, so we will look at making them ourselves. This will be a time consuming exercise that is worth a try if you are inclined to experimentation.

Scientific glass columns are frequently filled with 6mm lengths of 6mm glass tubing. If you purchase a few lengths of 6mm glass tube, score it with a file 6mm from the end, it will break easily with a little sharp tap. Keep doing this until you have collected enough to nearly fill the reflux column, and you have your very own Raschig rings. Note: wear safety glasses and gloves to prevent injury. It has been said that the results between Raschig rings and most other column fillings is like comparing the difference concerning chalk and cheese.

Another successful column filling is the common or garden fowl house variety of stainless steel pot scrub scouring pad. They resemble the swarf that turns from a lathe. Stretch out the balls of metal turnings into cylindrical shapes. Gently insert them into the column, being sure to prevent compaction. These work well but are far more difficult to cleanse between distillations.

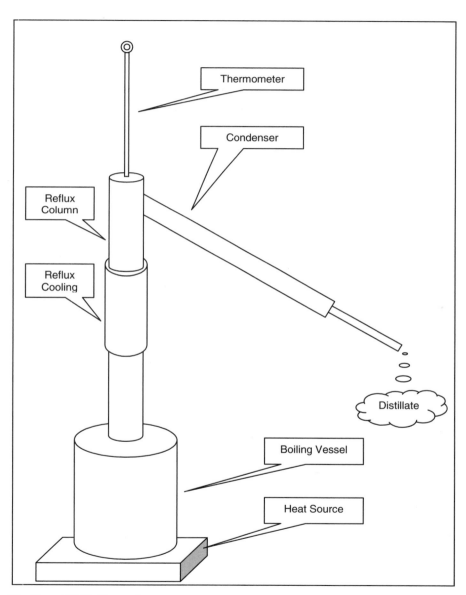

Reflux Still Drawing

Making Your Own Still

Making your own still is a relatively simple task that will be a rewarding exercise. It may not save you much money unless you can do most of it yourself. Using subcontractors for welding is a good idea if you are not proficient in TIG welding. The easiest task is drilling holes and bending tube. There are no exact measurements to worry about and workmanship is only a concern if you want your still to look beautiful. You don't even have to grind and polish it unless good looks are a consideration. We will look at two designs that will be easy to build and the 1st one can upgrade to the 2nd design without too much redundancy. Just a few basic tools will be required. Things like electric drill, sharp drill bits, hack saw, file. These articles are usually found in most handymen's sheds.

Firstly we will make the condenser as is common to both the simple (Pot) still and the Reflux Still. Next the construction of the complete simple Pot Still, then the complete Reflux Still. Although both stills are capable of being attached to a larger boiling vessel, for the exercise, we will look at affixing it to the common kitchen pressure cooker. The pressure cooker used for the original prototypes was a 5Ltr type as that size is tolerable by the Australian customs and excise folk. You will probably recognise it in some of the retailers from the photos on page 98 in this manual. Any old recycled or new pressure cooker will work well with the enclosed designs, as long as you can make the suggested modifications to it.

All stainless steel or copper tubular material is often purchased in inch sizes so both millimetre and inch sizes will be quoted. Tube is measured using outside dimensions. The wall thickness is 1.6mm of all tube used in this construction. When drilling holes, you should start with a small drill of 3mm to make a pilot hole then enlarge the hole to the correct size in 2mm steps. This is to avoid the drill from destroying the hole or making a triangular shape instead of a round hole. So when the text asks for a 10mm hole, start with 3mm then 5mm, 7mm, 9mm and 10mm drill bit to finish off the hole.

All stainless steel must be of food grade type 304 or 316. Some inferior grades of stainless steel tend to rust, especially when welded. The inner condenser tube should be of type 316 to be ideal.

The condenser is constructed completely of copper or stainless steel. It is the device that converts the vapour from the boiling vessel back into a liquid. Refer to Condenser Construction below for details.

If you desire to construct the entire Still of copper, then substitute all mention of stainless steel to copper. But remember that no brass threads are to be substitutes as they contain zinc and not of food quality material.

Condenser Construction - Warning, no solder to be used.

This condenser design is used in both the simple Pot Still and the Reflux design. All material is stainless steel type 304 or 316 (food grade), or copper.

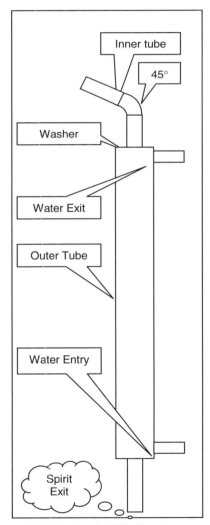

Cut a piece of 25mm (1") tube to a length of 350mm. File both ends so that they are square and smooth. 10mm from one end drill a 10mm hole. At the opposite end drill another 10mm hole, 10mm from that end. This completes the *outer tube* ready for assembly.

The *inner tube* is 12mm ($\frac{1}{2}$"). Now cut a 480mm length and make a 45 Deg bend very close to one end so that the complete bend occupies only 80mm. Borrow a plumbers tube bender for this.

Cut two lengths of 10mm ($\frac{3}{8}$") tube to a length of 20mm. These will be used for the cooling *water entry* and *water exit*.

All ends of tubing should be filed or ground so that they are square and smooth. Remove all sharp edges.

Weld the two 10mm *water tubes* to the holes in the *outer 25mm tube*. Remove any excess tubing inside the outer tube with a file.

Using two 12mm by 25mm ($\frac{1}{2}$" x 1") stainless washers, for the ends of the *outer tube*, mount the inner tube as per the drawing, making sure that the bend of the inner tube, bends away from the *water tubes* at the top of the *outer tube*. If everything fits, then weld both ends.

Obviously, all TIG welds must be of food quality material and completely sealed to stop leaks. You can grind and polish the welds if desired. This Condenser will be welded at 45 Deg from the vertical column attached to the boiling vessel. Solder joints are totally banned for assembly because solder contains lead, and that is not food quality.

Simple Pot Still Column

The Pot Still column is used for coupling the Boiling Vessel to the Condenser and the thermometer. Most Pot Stills do not use a thermometer but we have included a method of monitoring the temperature, as this will give you a far superior spirit than these others on the market.

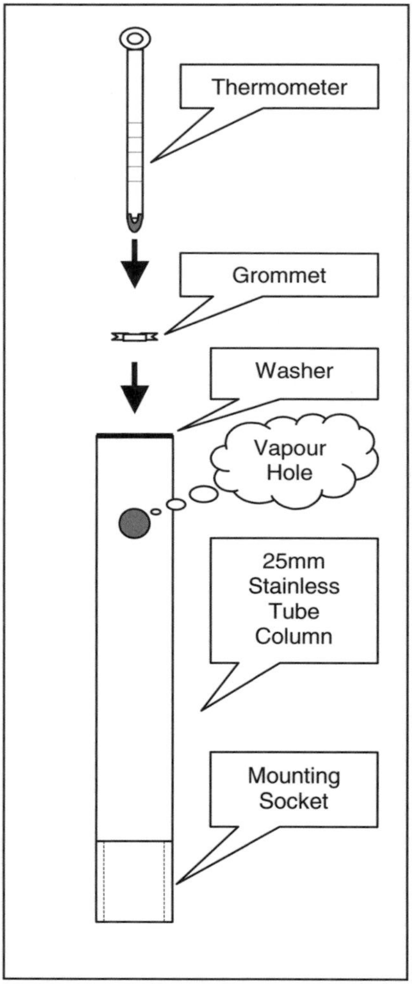

Thermometer

Grommet

Washer

Vapour Hole

25mm Stainless Tube Column

Mounting Socket

At the top of this *column* there is a rubber *grommet* inserted into a *washer* that is welded to the column top. Into this *grommet*, you can insert your accurate *thermometer*.

The *column* is 25mm (1") tube cut to a length of 150 mm. A 12mm by 25mm ($\frac{1}{2}$" x 1") stainless *washer* is used to seal the top of the *column*. The 12mm *vapour hole* is drilled 20mm from the top. Mounting of the condenser is accomplished by welding the 45 Deg end of the inner tube to the *vapour hole*, making sure that all rough ends are filed from inside the *column*. The condenser hangs down at a 45 Deg angle to allow the spirit to descend down through the inner tube at a slow rate for cooling.

A *Mounting Socket* is butt welded to the bottom of the *Column* so that it can be attached on to the Boiling Vessel. It is a standard $\frac{1}{2}$" pipe thread and made of stainless steel. It is threaded all the way through. These sockets are available from stainless steel stockists.

The stainless steel Washer at the column top is available from Nut and Bolt shops and is a standard size.

All stainless steel tubing is available from a specialist Stainless Steel stockist in most capital cities at a reasonable cost. Please remember that if your Still is constructed of copper, you must use food grade rods for welding. No brass or lead can be tolerated.

Assembled Simple (Pot) Still

The assembled Simple (Pot) Still shows the Condenser on page 59 welded to the Column on page 60. These welds, as all other welds, are welded using a TIG welder and stainless steel 316 rod.

This is a diagrammatical representation of the completed Simple Still. The 45° bend at the top of the Condenser is actually a gradual bend that was bent using a plumbers bending tool. A thermometer is placed at the column top using a rubber grommet. If you wish, a rubber bung can be used at the column top instead of welding a washer, then the thermometer inserted through the bunghole. Locating a bung of suitable size may be difficult as most of the hole sizes are unsuitable for thermometers.

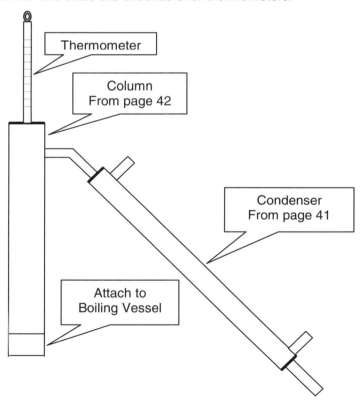

This completes the construction of the Simple (Pot) Still.

Reflux Still Column

Refer to: Reflux Still Column Drawing on page 63

The Reflux column described here is used to couple the boiling vessel to the condenser. For this diagram, we are not displaying the thermometer, but it should be inserted into the column top in a similar manner to the Simple Still column on page 60.

The *column* is 50mm (2") tube cut to a length of 550 mm. A 50mm by 25mm washer, then a 12mm by 25mm ($\frac{1}{2}$" x 1") stainless *washer* is used to seal the top of the *Reflux Column* ready for the thermometer.

The 12mm *vapour hole* is drilled 20mm from the top.

Four cooling tubes, each 10mm ($\frac{3}{8}$"), are mounted through the Column. The Lower tube is 100mm from the bottom, then 200mm, 300mm and 400 mm from the bottom.

The *Triclover* milking machine connector is shown without the coupling clamp and Teflon washer. The top section is welded to the *column* and the bottom to the top of the *Boiling Vessel*. You can purchase it in parts so that you can have more than one Boiling Vessel, as you may want to expand in the future.

Before using, this column will be $\frac{3}{4}$ full of glass marbles.

The Filling Withholding Plate is described after the Reflux Still Column Drawing on page 63.

Plumbing Your Still

Plumbing of the simple Pot Still is quite simple. It is just a matter of connecting the cold water to the lower part of the Condenser and the water will exit from the top end. There is only one thing to remember, and that is the cold water enters at the lowest point and exits from the highest point. By doing this, we achieve the cold end of the Condenser at the exit point of the spirit. So now we will have cold spirit emerging from the Condenser.

The Reflux Column is plumbed in a similar fashion. Depending on the construction of your Reflux Column, the actual connections may vary somewhat. The easiest thing to remember is that the cold water normally enters at the bottom and the warm water exits from the top. In this way we do not experience air bubbles in the plumbing.

When plumbing a Reflux Still, normally we hook up the cold water firstly to the Condenser section. The output from that will enter the Reflux Column at the bottom. This achieves the correct heat relationship between the Reflux Column and the Condenser.

Reflux Still Column Drawing

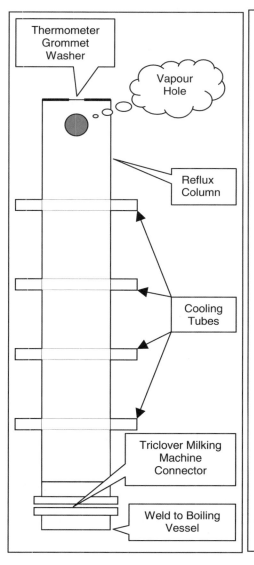

The Cooling Tubes on this particular column differ somewhat from normal.

The cool water, from the top of the Condenser, enters the top cooling tube. Then these tubes are linked together, using plastic tubing downwards until the required cooling is established. The number of cooling tubes that you link up will depend on the amount of cooling required. In the tropics, where the water is warmer, maybe all tubes will be required. Conversely, the cooler climate will have colder water, so therefore only two tubes will be required. The number of tubes linked up will also depend on the amount of heat applied to the Boiling Vessel. In this way, we have a completely variable system, and adaptable to many situations.

If you require only two cooling tubes, then link the two bottom tubes only. Leave the two top tubes unused.

Bottom End of Reflux Column

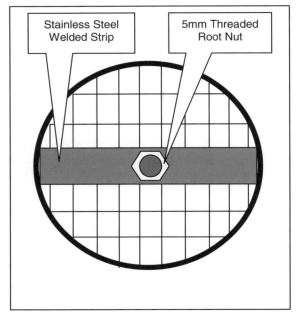

The bottom of the column has a removable perforated stainless steel plate or metal mesh fitted to retain the filling of glass marbles. It is held in place by a strip that is welded across the bottom inside of the Reflux column.

On this strip is a 5mm root nut ready to accept a 5mm screw and washer. Removal of the screw allows you to detach the perforated plate and empty out the glass marbles for clean up.

Remember that all material is food quality 316 or 304 stainless steel and is TIG welded.

The root nut is either pressed or riveted to the strip before it is welded to the column bottom.

Bottom view of Column showing the Perforated Plate and withholding strip.

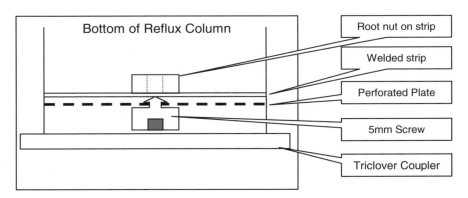

Assembled Reflux Still

The assembled Reflux Still shows the *Condenser* on page 59 welded to the Column on page 62. These welds, as all other welds, are welded using a TIG welder and stainless steel 316 rod.

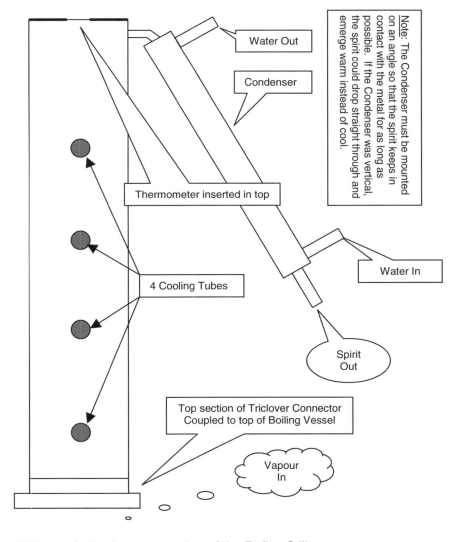

Water Out

Condenser

Note: The Condenser must be mounted on an angle so that the spirit keeps in contact with the metal for as long as possible. If the Condenser was vertical, the spirit could drop straight through and emerge warm instead of cool.

Thermometer inserted in top

Water In

4 Cooling Tubes

Spirit Out

Top section of Triclover Connector Coupled to top of Boiling Vessel

Vapour In

This concludes the construction of the Reflux Still.

Making a Boiling Vessel

You should review the section Distillation Pot (Boiling Vessel) on page 20 for an insight to Boiling Vessels as many topics are covered there.

In this section our main concern is making a Boiling Vessel from off-the-shelf items available from your local kitchenware super-store. Two methods will be presented, one small one for the legal constraints in Australia and one for the more adventurous.

Conversion of a Pressure Cooker

By far the easiest scheme is to produce a boiling vessel from your Pressure Cooker. Mum may be concerned for good reason. It should be a 5.5Ltr variety of stainless steel. The inside of this vessel needs to have a high water mark at 5Ltr. Not only because of the legal aspects but also to give some head room for expansion or frothing if that should occur. The only modification that needs to be performed is to transform the lid into a dual-purpose system of cooking and distillation.

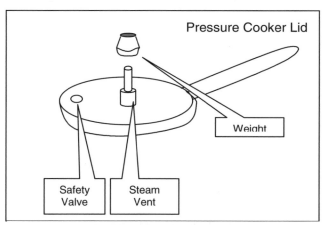

Pressure Cooker Lid

Weight

Safety
Valve

Steam
Vent

Remove the *Weight* and *Steam Vent* from the pressure cooker lid. These can be replaced later for Pot Still.

The *Safety Valve* should remain in place for safety reasons.

Refer to photograph on page 87

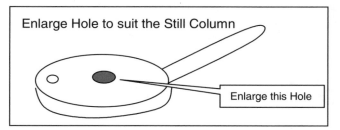

Enlarge Hole to suit the Still Column

Enlarge this Hole

Enlarge the Steam Vent hole to accept the mounting of the still column.

21 mm for the Pot Still or 50mm for the Reflux still.

After enlarging the hole in the Pressure Cooker lid, you are able to attach the Pot Still column by using a piece of $\frac{1}{2}$" or 12mm threaded pipe. Remember that 12mm pipe is measured as the inside diameter. The actual threaded section actually measures 21mm outside dimension.

Mounting of the Reflux Still column is a matter of welding the lower section of a Triclover milking machine coupler to the lid of the Pressure Cooker. This renders the Pressure Cooker useless as it was originally designed without some special engineering skills.

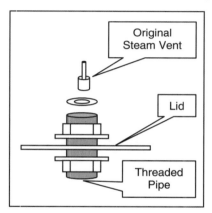

To convert Mums pressure Cooker back to original, all that is required is a washer welded to the top of some threaded tube and the original *Steam Vent* attached to the washer. The *Threaded Pipe* is the same size as the thread inside the Pot Still column; so two Backing Nuts will be employed to attach it back through lid's enlarged hole. It may look a little different, but will be functional. The *Threaded Pipe* is shown as shaded in the drawing with the two Backing Nuts, one on the top and one on the bottom of the Lid.

This completes the modification of a Pressure Cooker to a Boiling Vessel.

Pot Still Attachment

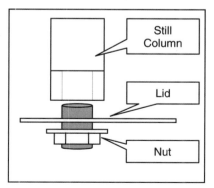

Making a Pot Still attachment is similar to the above drawing, except there is only one *Backing Nut* instead of two.

Naturally the Pot Still Column is shown shorter than actual size.

There should be a fibre washer sandwiched between the Pot Still Column and the Lid. This is also true for the above drawing.

Please Note: the threaded Pipe is $\frac{1}{2}$ Inch Pipe Thread, shaded in the drawing. Outside dimension is 21mm, inside 14mm. Very confusing?

Larger Boiling Vessel

The larger boiling vessel is for the serious Moonshiner; it will contain the total contents of your 25Ltr brew, so you will have only one distillation process per batch of fermentation.

This boiling vessel is fabricated from two, 15Ltr stainless steel Stock Pots, welded rim-to-rim. A heavy, cast bottom pot is desirable for strength on the top and even efficient heating underneath. The total capacity of the boiling vessel is 25 to 30 litres. These Stock Pots are available from the kitchenware section in larger supermarkets.

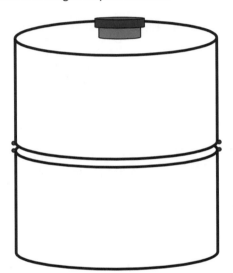

Bore a hole in the top to suit the bottom section of a milking machine Triclover coupler that is welded to the top of this vessel.

You can weld the two pots together or use a rubber gasket and a suitable drum lid cam operated clamp to hold them together. This would be easier cleaning.

There are boiling vessels available on the market from some brew shops with integral elements, which makes heating very efficient. The material on some of these vessels is very light and needs reinforcing with a large washer both above and below the lid when mounting your still column. The main advantage with these pots is there is no extra work to finish them. Beware, do not boil one of these dry else your heating element will burn out. Modifying a 30Ltr hot water urn is also worthwhile looking into. They have an integral, usually protected, heating element, but the lid needs better sealing. Making your own is far more rewarding and cost effective. It will also be unique.

Some folks have used a hot water cylinder for a large Boiling Vessel.

Triclover to Pipe Thread Converter

This converter can be used to couple a 2" Triclover coupling used on a large boiling vessel to a standard $\frac{1}{2}$ inch pipe thread used on the Pot Still.

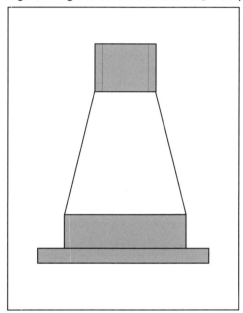

The top section is a standard $\frac{1}{2}$ inch male nipple pipe thread that will screw into the Pot Still Column. The outside diameter of this thread is 21mm, welded to the tube adaptor.

This adaptor is used to reduce a 2-inch (50mm) Tube to the $\frac{1}{2}$ inch Pipe. Dimensions are 50mm to 19mm in metric. These are off-the-shelf in most stainless steel dealers.

The bottom section is a standard milking machine part used to make up a complete Triclover coupler. These are available from both stainless steel stockists and milking machine parts dealers. To stop the confusion between Pipe and Tube measurements, Pipe is measured as inside diameter and Tube as outside measurement. By butt-welding these two, pipe-to-tube, we can use both technologies.

If you find difficulty purchasing some of the stainless steel parts in your neck of the woods, you can look at using some copper fittings. Once fabricated, all copper material can be either chrome or nickel-plated. Because the purist's for food quality frown upon brass, this should be your last choice, and must be nickel-plated.

As an example of this, the Pot Still Attachment on page 67 can be fabricated from a 20mm length of $\frac{1}{2}$ inch-threaded pipe and a backing nut from your local plumbers supply. The exact length depends on the thickness of the boiling vessel top. Thread on the nut until flush with the lower end of the thread, flange upwards. Silver Solder the nut in place with food grade rod, no lead allowed. Nickel-plate the fabrication and the job is complete.

There is little cost saving between copper and stainless steel material.

Purification System

Back in section Carbon Purification on page 23, we touched on filtering our spirit to remove some of the nasties that cause hangovers and foul odours. In this section we become serious about that same matter.

One of the most important processes in the manufacture of spirit is the purification procedure. The purification process discussed on page 23 is simple and effective, but time consuming and not as efficient as what you are about to learn. This system is used worldwide and is successful for spirit concentrations of 50% or less. The only difference is that commercial spirit manufacturers filter their spirit from bottom to top, moving upwards through the activated carbon at a constant flow rate of from 0.2 to 0.5 metres per hour. We will mimic the flow rate, but downwards in a smaller column rather than upwards like our commercial counterparts.

The absorption capability of activated carbon can be likened to a sponge, full of microscopic holes that the impurities fasten to. These holes can be measured in metres squared per gram. A reasonable activated carbon will have a surface area from 500 to 1200 square metres per gram. The grain size should be around 1mm each. Larger grain sizes will work ineffectively. Although a grain size of 12 x 40 is not actually 1mm in size, it does work fine. This 12 x 40 is a measurement of a minimum of 12 grains per inch and a maximum of 40 grains per inch. So for those mathematicians out there, we required 25.4 grains per inch for a grain size of 1mm. So 12 is less than 25.4 and 40 is greater than 25.4 per inch.

This sponge like structure in the activated carbon absorbs the impurities. These include fusel oils and the flavour of yeast. Odours are also removed. One should filter slowly through a layer of activated carbon around 1 metre in depth, or greater. There are many books on this subject, so read plenty if possible. The system discussed here is an abridged version that will work extremely well for the home distiller who is serious about his Moonshine.

Reactivation of your spent carbon is a futile exercise. During the manufacture of the carbon, raw materials such as coconut shells, coconut husks, peat or coal are heated to around 1000° C, without oxygen, to drive off all the unwanted gasses and tars. It is then activated using superheated steam at 130° C. So it cannot be reactivated in the oven or sunshine. Best not waste your time trying. Buy some from a carbon supplier. A 25Kg bag if you are a serious Moonshiner, as the price drops for this quantity.

Make your own Filter

Although stainless steel is an ideal material for this project, we will make this one from cost effective plastic pipe. Food grade plastic should be used. PVC is not a desirable material for this filter.

The top section is fabricated using reducing tapers from your plumber's store. Starting with a 150mm X 100mm taper, then that fits inside a

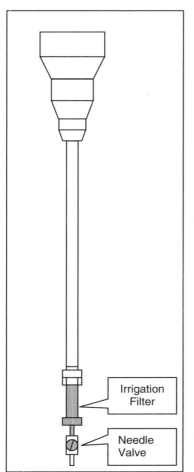

100mm X 50mm taper. The final taper is a 50 X 40mm taper reducer. These are all standard fittings at a reasonable cost. They are all glued together or plastic welded.

Because of height constraints in most buildings, we will use a 1m length of 40mm pipe for the next section. 1.5 to 2m would be ideal, but 1m works real well with good quality activated carbon.

Towards the bottom, glue a 40mm x 40mm pipe to thread coupler. Screwed into this coupler is a Poly 40mm X 25mm thread adaptor. Now this leaves you with a 25mm (1") female pipe thread.

Into this thread, screw a 19mm inline *Irrigation Filter*. Make sure that you obtain one with a 25mm thread at both ends. Probably this filter will be upside down as the flow arrow indicates. It is used upside down to stop any carbon from escaping out the bottom into the *Needle Valve*. You will remove the inner section of this filter to clean out the column during for carbon replacement.

Irrigation Filter

Needle Valve

The final component is a plastic *Needle Valve*, micro irrigation type, to adjust the flow rate of the spirit through the filter column. It is coupled to the *Irrigation Filter* using a piece of garden hose.

The plastic version of this filter is extremely cost effective and can be constructed in only one hour. Go for it! Then make a stainless version.

Mounting of the filter is accomplished using a metal clamp around the 150mm section and attach it to a wall with a wooden spacer. The spacer allows for some distance from the wall, so that you can use a 15 to 19Ltr water container inverted and inserted into the top of this filter funnel.

Operating your Filter

There are two methods of using this filter. Firstly you can just pour your spirit in the top section using it as a funnel. Secondly, obtain two 15 or 19Ltr drinking water bottles. They are the variety that you see in many office situations, upside down, in cold drinking water dispensers. Place an empty one at the bottom of the filter and the other up side down with its neck into the funnel section. As the filter requires more spirit, it will dispense from the upper bottle automatically. If this situation scares you, try to experiment with water only, no carbon, until you gain some confidence that it works. Also this training period will prove to you that there are no leaks in your newly created filter masterpiece.

Pour 1.25Ltr of activated carbon into the top of your filter, as this will fill the 40mm section only. Place an empty container at the collection point, bottom of the filter. Close the needle valve. Upend the whole container of spirit into the top funnel section and let it rest up side down on the rim of the funnel. As the spirit is required, it will exit from the upper container. Now adjust the needle valve to collect 500ml per hour, which is 0.4 meters per hour through the activated carbon. A rate of 0.2 to 0.5 meters per hour is recommended, depending on the quality of your activated carbon.

Most carbon is clean, but if you have some black suspensions from your carbon, you can recycle the 1st, black portion back into your filter. Another popular method is to run the filter outlet through a coffee filter paper until clean spirit emerges. One pass through this filter will produce tremendous results in most cases. The 1.25Ltr of activated carbon will filter the total contents of a 15 or 19Ltr water container full of spirit.

You should never pour the filtered spirit back through your filter, as this will degrade your finely filtered spirit. There is however, a method of using your activated carbon extremely efficiently by effectively recycling it.

Save the carbon in the filter for the next filtration. Now firstly filter your spirit through the old carbon, and then discard it. Refill the filter and pass the same spirit back through the new carbon. This is the connoisseur's method of purification. This way you achieve fantastic results without using any extra carbon. Highly recommended for superior quality spirit.

Cooling Water System

Recycled Water System

For those of you who have difficulty in justifying throwing away precious water from your household supply connected to the water mains, or folks who use bore or tank water with an electric pump, here is a solution that will cure your challenges. It's simple and cheap to fabricate from recycled components and is operated from a 12-volt DC supply for safety.

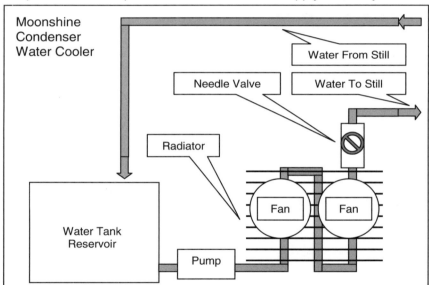

The *Water Tank* can be any container that will hold 10 to 20 litres of garden tap water. A 12 Volt car type petrol *Pump* is employed to circulate the cooling water through a *Radiator*. Now the cooling water is connected to the condenser water input connection of your still via a *Needle Valve*. After the warm water leaves the still condenser, it is fed back to the *Water Tank* or Reservoir. An electric fuel pump of 130 litres per hour appears to be a standard type for 4X4 vehicles and is suitable. The Radiator can be either a car oil cooler or from an old air conditioner, with two 12 Volt computer fans attached for cooling. A needle valve is utilised to control the flow of water through the system at around 500ml per minute, which is only 30 ltres per hour.

A car battery or 12 Volt 3 to 5 Amp DC power supply is required.

Rainwater Tank System

The challenge that we encounter with farm tank rainwater situation is that we don't want to throw our cooling water away after leaving the still, and the major problem is that the existing pump will cycle on and off because the flow through our still is too small. We can use the system presented on the previous page so that we recycle the same water over and over, or we can make use of the existing pump used to supply water to our house.

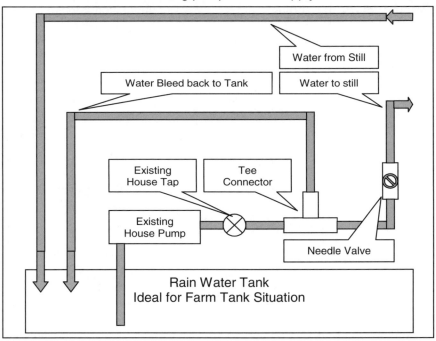

The operating principle of this drawing is to supply a small amount of water to the still without the *House Pump* cycling on and off. The *House Tap* is adjusted so that the pump keeps running continuously. The *Tee Connector* allows water to flow back to the tank for this purpose. Adjusting the *Needle Valve* will accomplish the small volume of water for the still cooling and condenser requirements.

Because of the large volume in the *Rain Water Tank*, we are not required to cool the water as the previous page drawing described. This may be a little wasteful for the size of the pump, but it will work. No water is wasted.

Danger, Accidents and Law Reform

Implosion

Your boiling vessel can implode immediately after the heat source is removed if precautions are not observed. As the boiling vessel cools, a vacuum forms inside if air cannot enter back through the distillation column. A cause of this predicament is when the spirit hose gets kinked during cooling down. If this is the case, the boiling vessel will shrink into a stainless steel duster, especially if your boiling vessel is of flimsy material.

Immediately after the heat is removed, one must remove the tube from the spirit outlet of the condenser section of the still to allow uninhibited air to enter the system. The vacuum forms without delay once the heat is removed.

Explosion

Spirit vapour is highly explosive. Explosive alcohol gas can leak from your still if it is not tightly connected to the boiling vessel or you start distillation without commencing the flow of cooling water. Also if the spirit outlet hose drops off, alcohol can drip onto the heating source, causing formation of gas.

This gas is extremely explosive, so be careful connecting the hoses and setting up your apparatus ready for distillation. Make sure everything is tight and cooling water is flowing.

Fire Risk

Electrical heat source is safer than the open flame for distillation. If one uses gas heating, then extra care must be taken that your still is not left unattended, as the overflowing alcohol will ignite, causing much heat and risk of a large fire. Spirit vapour is highly explosive.

Smoking during distillation can be risky, especially if you sample the proceeds during the procedure. Even with cooling water running, the spirit is flammable.

Flooding

Flooding is not so serious, but can occur if the cooling water hoses are not attached too well. A blocked drain, or the outlet hose falls from the drainage system can be a cause.

There should be good quality hose clips attaching the cooling water system, as well as the connection to the water tap. All hoses should be in good condition, fit well and be the correct size for the task.

Alcoholic Poisoning

There can be much discussion on the subject of alcoholic Poisoning. Normally we consume our spirit in controlled moderation so that this cannot occur. 50% spirit, or greater, can be very dangerous as we are unable to digest high concentrations easily.

However, one can guzzle at an alarming uncontrolled rate and cause many hangovers and headaches with ones spouse and loved ones. It has been written that Poisoning from ethyl alcohol can never come to pass. I don't think that we need to prove that statement.

Law of producing Moonshine

The knowledge of how to produce Moonshine is not an offence in countries with freedom of press and speech. The reader is urged to follow the current laws that apply in your country. Some countries are in a process of updating their laws to allow small production of alcohol for their own consumption. Beer and Wine production has been relaxed in many countries. Maybe the production of these beverages, then refining into a pure spirit using distillation will follow.

Write letters, tell your politicians, write to the newspapers, make your point known, work democratically to reform. But before doing so, be well informed; read the section, More on Health Issues on page 77 for a further understanding.

More on Health Issues

One of the infamous claims made by certain folks when the subject of home brewing and distillation is being conversed, is that people are liable to poison themselves. Specifically, there would be a danger of going blind. Examples of this having happened to individuals or even whole communities, or even tribes, in various countries around the world are cited. But when the specifics are asked, they all run for cover, for it is all very reminiscent of the Indian Rope Trick. Everyone has heard about it, but no one has actually seen it. The fact of the matter is that it would be virtually impossible to poison oneself by drinking home-distilled spirits, especially diluted down to 40% alcohol. Distillation in itself does not produce anything, so there can be nothing in a distilled spirit that was not already in the original beer or wine. How can one convert a harmless beverage, such as wine or beer, into a lethal poison by simply boiling it? Of course wine and beer does contain poisonous methanol and fusel oils as an example. But their harmful effect is to produce headaches and hangovers that people experience if they over indulge.

Distillation purifies the brew by separating these unwanted chemicals, permitting them to be discarded. They smell similar to paint stripper. So, to poison oneself, it would be necessary to remove these nasties from both wine and beer by distillation, pour the purified ethyl alcohol down the drain, then, ignoring the pungent smell and sickening taste, drink the paint stripper. This is about as likely as cooking a cockatoo in the saucepan with a large rock, checking when the rock is tender, chucking the cockatoo, and then eating the rock. Sounds incredible, doesn't it!

Headaches and hangovers are well known consequences of over indulgent drinking of alcohol. But what is less well known is that the unpleasant side effects are largely due to the impurities including many preservatives, and not the alcohol per se.

This interesting fact can be confirmed by many folks who habitually consume a large amount of rum or whisky from a commercial source, then ask them to devour a similar quantity of home produced spirit of the same type. Numerous studies have been made and all investigations point to the same thing, i.e. that the symptoms of hangover, headaches, halitosis, gastric irritations, fatigue and dizziness, were far more severe when the same amount of alcohol was consumed in the form of whisky than in the form of vodka, both of commercial origin. Sit down with a friend and try the same experiment, substituting the vodka with homemade spirit. You will be pleasantly surprised.

The effects described were produced by commercial whisky and rum in which the offending chemicals occurred at about 3%. These substances add to the taste of not only whiskey and rum, but wine and beer also. Many of the subtle tastes are from fusel oils that exist after fermentation. The chief culprit among the fusel oils is considered to be amyl alcohol. These results are not really definitive. Even without a trial, it is not difficult to believe that drinking such things as methanol and fusel oils, even in small amounts, will be detrimental to good health.

One of the conclusions to be drawn from this discussion is that whisky production, using traditional means, should be avoided at all costs by amateurs. Not only is it difficult to produce a blend of alcohol and other tastes to give a palatable beverage, but also additionally, the consequences of error could be unpleasant. It would be far more sensible to remove all the impurities by fractional distillation using a Reflux Still, to produce pure alcohol and then add flavouring by the addition of a known essence. Such a beverage may not be identical to its commercial counterpart, but it will be absolutely safe. Remember that not all Gins taste alike; they all have slightly different flavours. You will probably produce a unique blend, far superior to the commercial equivalent.

One final comment is needed on the question of alcohol concentrations in alcoholic beverages. Beer alcohol concentration is around 5%, wine ranges from 8 to 13%, while distilled spirit is usually 40%. Only one moment's thought is required to appreciate that the alcoholic concentration in a drink is irrelevant. It is the amount that is consumed that is the determining factor in whether a person becomes inebriated. Drinking a bottle of beer at 5% concentration is not less harmful than a $1\frac{1}{2}$ oz swig of 40% whisky just because the beer is weaker. They both contain a similar amount of alcohol, around 17ml. Adding a goodly splash of water to your whisky, or waiting for the ice to melt, dilutes the whisky to maybe 6%; the amount of alcohol remains unchanged.

Just because beer has 5% alcohol and spirits have 40% does not mean that the Bourbon drinker is eight times more likely to over indulge than the beer drinker. People drink until they've had enough, or feel in a certain mood. If this takes five, ten or even more beers, then that is the number that will be drunk. The fact of the matter is that beer drinkers invariably cause many of the anti-social behaviours in public places and sporting complexes. Many studies of drinking and driving have shown that the vast majority of those pulled over have been drinking beer, not spirits. It's the testosterone level that causes the problem, not the alcohol intensity.

When All Else Fails

Fermentation Has Stuck

In most cases, a vigorous stir should get the yeast working again, but in some cases you may need to add some EC1118 alcohol tolerant yeast. Possibly moving your brew to a warmer position and a good stir up will get it going again. An inexpensive stick-on thermometer, available from your local brew shop, will help monitor the temperature situation.

Adding more sugar to get the fermentation going again is a trick that a beer brewer may use. Unfortunately this is not such a good idea for alcohol brews of sugar and water. When you set down your brew, the sugar level was calculated so it would be completely exhausted at the same time as the yeast quits. The alcohol content has peaked, disabling the yeast. This is not only wasteful but can lead to frothing in the boiling vessel during distillation. It will also mess up your hydrometer readings.

The Wash Won't Clear

Usually moving your fully worked out brew into a cool place or fridge will help this situation. You can review the section Following Fermentation on page 18 to better understand the process of clearing your fermented Wash.

Distillation Won't Start

Check that the temperature of your Wash is rising in the boiling vessel. The heat source may not be of sufficient size or wattage to heat your boiling vessel. Is the heat controller fully on? Does your boiling vessel contain fermented Wash with alcohol? Use your hydrometer to check the specific gravity; it should be around 990 when at 20° C. Is the cooling water flowing at around 500ml per minute or greater? Is there a clear passage for the distillate to flow from the condenser?

Cloudy or Contaminated Spirit Flows

May be there is not enough space between the Wash surface and the top of your boiling vessel. If frothing occurs then there may be some sugar left in the Wash that was unfermented. An anti foaming agent would help this situation. The column filling may be grubby from the last distillation. So clean or change it. Check that the temperature has not exceeded 92° C and the fusel oils are not flowing.

Surge Boiling of the Wash

The thermostat controlling the temperature has too high a differential between switching off to switch back on again. Replace the thermostat with a Triac type controller. The cooling water may be reversed; dread the thought! Check the instructions that came with your still to make sure that it is hooked up correctly. There should be from 100 to 200mm of space above the Wash to the lid of the boiling vessel. A whole heap of marbles in the bottom of your boiling vessel can spread the head evenly across the bottom. These will act as boiling stones. Using water from a well or rainwater tank with a pump cycling on and off will cause surging in temperature. The section on Cooling Water System on page 73 will help this situation.

Alcohol Percentage is Low

The temperature at the still head is too high and the output is nearly exhausted. Keep the temperature from 75 to 92° C. Take your sample for testing directly from the condenser output, not from the collecting jar. There may be no alcohol in your Wash.

Not Enough Alcohol

Approximately 10 to 20% of your total volume of Wash should pour from the output of the condenser at a total average percentage of 70 to 94%. If the output is less than that, the cause is usually because the Wash did not fully work out. Poor yeast or incorrect temperature can be the culprit. Use new well-known turbo brands instead of old bread yeast. Checking with your hydrometer before and after fermentation is a wise move. Do not add sugar in excess of what the yeast can handle, as this will cause other problems like foaming in the boiling vessel.

Smells Real Bad, Tastes Foul

Too higher temperature in the boiling vessel can rupture the yeast buds and pollute the Wash. Make sure that your Wash has settled and been siphoned off before distillation. Sometimes if there is too much Mash in your Wash it can burn and stick to the bottom of your boiling vessel, producing a foul burnt smell.

Make sure there is new activated carbon for your filtering system. Remember that the slower the better for filtering and purification. Use the correct grade of activated carbon. Read Purification System on page 70.

Filtered Spirit is Cloudy

The most probable cause of cloudy spirit from your purification system is usually because there was a lot of carbon dust in the activated carbon that you were using. Normally this will settle if given enough time. There are two cures for this situation. Firstly purchase clean activated carbon. Secondly you can siphon off the clean spirit, then filter the remainder through some coffee filter paper before adding it to the already clean spirit. An excellent technique is to keep the carbon polluted spirit, which will normally be a small amount left at the bottom of the bottle, and blend it with the next filtration after filtering through coffee filter paper. In this way you can wait a few weeks for it to settle as the next brew comes along.

Rum Doesn't Taste Like Rum

Well here we have a dilemma. Before trying to make Rum using your own methods, you ought to take the easy path to success. Firstly one must make pure spirit as outlined in this manual. Then add some known spirit essences to that spirit. If you are still disappointed, try a different essence. Then try a different brand. Make sure that your spirit is around 37% alcohol content before attempting to make over-proof spirit.

If you are not using essences to flavour your spirit, then you're on your own. But don't be discouraged, experiment a little at a time and you will get your own unique flavour and bouquet. Remember that all famous spirit makers had humble beginnings.

Spirit Burns My Throat

There is a simple cure. Start with 37% spirit before trying to make over-proof 51% beverages.

Liqueurs are Not Thick Enough

Add corn syrup, either thick liquid or powdered to your liqueur. Also many liqueurs have added sugar. When measuring the water to be added to dilute the spirit, allow for the corn syrup quantity in you calculation to be included in the water quantity. Remember, you cannot measure the alcoholic content with an alcometer once you have mixed sugar and/or corn syrup with your raw spirit.

My Hangover Hurts

Too bad, sleep it off and next time drink less commercial spirit!

Gasohol - Alternative to Motor Fuel

What is Gasohol? A mixture of Gasoline and Alcohol.

Gasohol is an accepted name for motor fuel when Ethanol and Petrol are mixed together at a rate of 10% ethanol and 90% petrol to produce a cleaner and possibly more cost effective fuel for motor vehicles. It can be used without motor modifications when up to 25% ethanol is mixed with petrol, or it can be used straight with a modified engine. It burns cooler and will produce less offensive exhaust emissions. Many folk say that it will be the engine fuel of the future. What we will look at in this manual is a cost effective method of producing ethanol that is suitable for engine, but not human consumption.

Ethanol absorbs water and will always contain water. There is no problem with that because in some cases it actually improves the fuel. Some of you may remember some years ago that one could add a water injector to your car engine. This was often to the amusement of onlookers watching the tremendous amount of steam emerging from the exhaust pipe. When starting to use ethanol for the first time, it is advisable to add a small quantity, and then slowly increase the percentage to 25%. This will strip out any residual water lying at the bottom of your petrol tank. Otherwise there may be some engine hiccups and misfiring raising the curiosity among your many neighbours. A good starting point is 10% ethanol and 90% petrol until you gain confidence. At a later stage, you may wish to convert over to 100% ethanol, but that will require enlarging your carburettor jets somewhat.

Making the Ethanol for Gasohol

Making the ethanol is covered in section Making HokiNooki Moonshine on page 34. The only difference is that this time we are not too worried about the type of grain that we use. Barley is possibly the easiest one to make the malt that is necessary for the malting of the rest of the grain. Potatoes, Barley, Corn (Maize), Rye Wheat and Rice are among the favourites. Molasses mixed with water at a ratio of 25% to 75% is also a consideration. Because of the large amount of leftovers after fermentation, one should look at using this high protein residue as a cattle feed supplement. Review the section Traditional Whisky or Bourbon (Sugarless) on page 36 for instructions on malting and fermenting the required mash. Alcohol can also be made from whey containing lactose.

The actual distillation process will be discussed in more detail in this section because we need to reduce the cost of production, to make gasohol worthwhile.

Distillation of Ethanol for Gasohol

Distillation of gasohol requires a vastly different system to that of potable spirits. Fractional distillation in a large continuous system would be the ideal system, but too costly to set up for our small production. We will look at construction of a Solar Still that is rather different to those discussed earlier. Again I must emphasise that this Still must not be used for producing spirit for human consumption. The temperatures that we learned about earlier are much the same for distillation. Ethyl alcohol evaporates at 78° C but this time we will be unable to control the temperature so precisely because we are in the lap of the gods for our sun as our heat source.

The previously discussed stills will work fine except the cost to operate the heating system. Try to use some of your spirit from those stills, if you have one, to gain confidence on the production of gasohol before making the Solar Still. With the Solar Still you will be required to repeat the distillation process more than once to raise the percentage of alcohol to a reasonable level of greater than 70% alcohol in water before mixing it with petrol.

Pay particular attention to filtering out the residue and floaters from your fermented mash, otherwise you will clog up and pollute your Solar Still. On a hot sunny day, the sun will perform some sterilization for you, but during the hours of darkness, who knows what may grow inside your Still. You may have a fine crop of tomatoes growing inside your Still one morning, or even worse some incurable fungus or unknown mushrooms and toadstools.

We will make it from plywood with an inclined glass top. The whole contraption will be sealed with a caulking compound such as silicon or wallboard adhesive. This caulking compound and any other adhesives need to be of a waterproof variety. The Wash will be trickled into this box that is angled to the sun at 90 Deg. This angle may be a problem in the tropics as the angle there may be horizontal to the ground. We require around 45 Deg for the distillation to work properly, so a little experimentation may be required. In the tropics, an angle of say 45 Deg will probably work well because there will be a greater ambient heat available. The base of the box will be lined with thin black felt or similar, and the insides will be painted matt black except for the glass lid. The removable lid, for cleaning purposes, is sealed with a suitable rubber gasket. Heat of the sun will vaporise the alcohol, which will condense on the underside of the glass lid and will descend down the inclined glass into a collection trough. There will also be some excess water that will require draining off frequently via a separate draining cock.

As mentioned earlier, you will need to repeat the same batch of alcohol to raise the percentage to around 70% or greater. This will be checked with your alcometer (alcohol hydrometer) that was used to make your potable alcohol in section Alcometer or Spirit Hydrometer on page 20.

Always keep in mind that this Still is very basic and as such it is not 100% efficient. In earlier sections you would have read that ethyl alcohol vaporises at 78° C, whereas water boils at 100° C. So in a temperature controlled system, the temperature of the Wash is kept close as possible to produce 78° C at the head of the Still. On this basic solar design, there is no prevision made for such luxuries. So some problems may occur.

- You will have a higher than desired water content in your resultant distillate as the alcohol and water in the Wash solution will both be vaporising simultaneously resulting in too much water. This will depend on the sun's heat and flow rate through the Solar Still.

- The waste from the Wash emerging from the bottom of the Still will often have a certain residual percentage of alcohol. In a similar manner to the above comment, this will also depend on the heat and flow rate discussed.

The procedure to rectify this dilemma after discovering that there is greater than 2% alcohol present in your waste Wash is:

- Re-distillation of the waste Wash.

- Slow down the flow rate of your Wash for the first run through the Solar Still. A small tap fitted on the inlet line to control the throughput accomplishes this. There is no real method of automation.

Once you have mastered the flow control of this Still, remember it is cheap to run, you can process the results through a normal Still that is described earlier in this manual under Distillation on page 19. For the heat source, if you are on a farm, try using a wood fire. At least the bulk of the spirit will have been removed using your Solar Still. The cost of running a normal Pot or Reflux Still for the last refinement is worth consideration.

Please remember that this type of Still leaves a lot to be desired in regards to sterilization and filtering. Even if the alcohol fails to kill you, there is likelihood of leaving you with poor eyesight.

Pollution Issues

As opposed to petroleum products, ethanol burns cleanly and it contains a large percentage of its own requirement of oxygen for combustion, as contrasting with petroleum products that require twice as much oxygen from the atmosphere for burning. This is why many rocket engines have been designed to burn a mixture of liquid oxygen and alcohol for their fuel. The waste products emitting from the exhaust from the combustion of alcohol are primarily carbon dioxide and water. We can do with the water and the plants will enjoy the CO_2. This is different to the pollutant sulphur dioxide from gasoline engines. Carbon monoxide, CO, is of great concern as a pollutant. Gasoline engines can produce from 5 to 10% CO which is very toxic to animal life. One should expect far less than one percent of CO for combustion of alcohol. Just for interest sake, the red cells in our blood (haemoglobin) will assimilate CO far more easily than oxygen. These red cells normally carry oxygen for us to sustain life. When carbon monoxide is present, they will prefer to absorb CO in place of our required oxygen. If this situation persists, we will die from of lack of oxygen being absorbed via our lungs. Alcohol burns easily and completely without pollution issues.

Solar Still Box

This box measures 2400mm X 1200mm. The height of the sides measure 200mm. A partition is fitted 150mm from the front or bottom end, with a height of 150mm so that it is 50mm from the glass or plexiglass plate fitted to the upper surface. There is a 12mm tube fitted to the bottom right corner that allows the alcohol to drain out, and another mounted above the partition that permits the extraction of the spent Wash. Heavy black cloth or felt is lying on the bottom of the box, above the partition that will be soaked with the incoming Wash. At the top right is the Wash entrance tube, which is connected to a perforated tube inside the box that allows Wash to trickle down over the black cloth. The perforated tube inside the box will evenly distribute the incoming Wash.

Plan View of the Solar Still

This plan view displays the partition that is fitted 150mm up from the bottom. It is 150mm high so as to clear the glass top plate by 50mm.

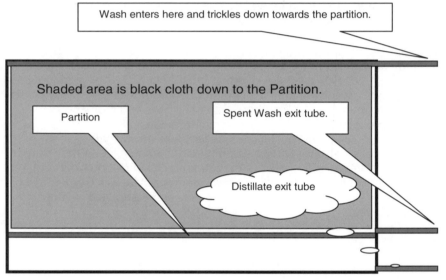

Wash enters here and trickles down towards the partition.

Shaded area is black cloth down to the Partition.

Partition

Spent Wash exit tube.

Distillate exit tube

The measurement of this box is 2400mm X 1200mm and is constructed from 19mm water tolerant plywood. A glass plate is rubber sealed on top.

End View of Solar Still

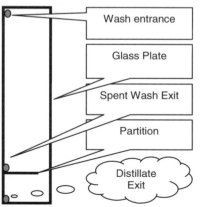

Wash entrance

Glass Plate

Spent Wash Exit

Partition

Distillate Exit

This Still is angled 45 Deg from vertical facing the sun. A sealed glass plate mounted on top of the Still will condense the evaporated alcohol that will run down to the Distillate Exit tube. Spent Wash will exit above the partition after trickling down through the black cloth, which covers from the top of the box to the partition.

The Wash entrance tube is perforated along the entire length to allow the Wash to distribute evenly across the black cloth.

These drawings are not to scale.

If desired, you could paint the lower portion of the glass plate, below the partition, with silver tinted paint. This would help keep the alcohol collection trough cooler than the rest of the Still.

It is the intention of this Gasohol section to get some people interested in production of alcohol for automobiles and other engines. The Solar Still presented here is to help some of you get started in an alternative fuel as the price for a litre of petrol is soaring by the day. In the foreseeable future petrol will be out of the reach of the average person, so hopefully this manual will encourage some of you to experiment.

The Solar Still outlined in this manual, as far as I know, has not been assembled and tried, but the principle will work. The finer details for sealing the glass has been omitted because of the above reason. There is also need for some thought about automating the injection of the Wash, and distributing it evenly across the black cloth, for efficient production. I believe that with a little adventurous knowledge and skill the drawing can be improved upon to a fully working and marketable system of alcohol production for automobiles. With this in mind, I would welcome any feedback on improvements of the design, and low costs methods of producing alcohol for automobiles. Many of the sugar refineries are using their molasses for alcohol production along with some butter manufacturers using whey lactose for the same. I would welcome any knowledge of these two methods, as they are both waste products from their primary production of sugar or butter or cheese respectively.

In some countries it may be illegal to produce such a Still without licensing, so I do not want to encourage any of you to break the law as it stands. I also believe that government officials would be lenient towards granting a license if one could prove that it was for a good cause such as saving overseas funds for the importation of motor fuel.

The cost of producing such a still is very low because it can be manufactured from plywood and acrylic plastic instead of glass for the top. There is no secret of solar heating for hot water, so this is a simple adaptation of the same principal.

A better method for very high production would be a continuous fractional distillation column, but this would be out of reach for most home experimenters. To date of printing, I have not discovered any plans for a reasonable cost fractional distillation column, but if one comes my way, I will add it to this manual for later release. I feel sure that a fractional distillation column would work well using the alcohol produced, for the fuel to heat such a distillation system, or that other waste products such as methane could be used in the same manner.

Tables and Reference Section

Proof Table for Alcohol

There are differing systems of Proof in USA, Canada and Great Britain. All three types are referenced to the percentage of alcohol by volume in the beverage being measured. Both the Canadians and British use a scale called Sykes, but the Canadians use 100 Proof Sykes as their reference for over or under Proof. Therefore 99 Proof Sykes is under Proof and anything over Proof is greater than 100 Proof Sykes. The negative sign indicates under and the plus sign indicates over Proof.

Formula used: Sykes = Percent $\times$ 1.75, Canadian = Sykes − 100.

Percent By Volume	USA Proof	British Sykes	Canadian
2	4	3.5	-96.5
4	8	7.0	-93.0
6	12	10.5	-89.5
8	16	14.0	-86.0
10	20	17.5	-82.5
12	24	21.0	-79.0
14	28	24.5	-75.5
16	32	28.0	-72.0
18	36	31.5	-68.5
20	40	35.0	-65.0
25	50	43.8	-56.2
30	60	52.5	-47.5
35	70	61.3	-38.7
40	80	70.0	-30.0
45	90	78.8	-21.2
50	100	87.5	-12.5
60	120	105.0	+05.0
70	140	122.5	+22.5
80	160	140.0	+40.0
100	200	175.0	+75.0

Dilution Of Spirit With Water

This table will allow you to make 1Ltr of spirit at 40%

Original Alcohol Percentage	Ml of **Alcohol** to make 40%	Ml of **Water** to make 40%
40	1000	Zero
45	889	111
50	800	200
55	727	273
60	667	333
65	615	385
70	571	429
75	533	467
80	500	500

Temperature Conversion Table

C°	F°	C°	F°	C°	F°	C°	F°	C°	F°
15	59.0	31	87.8	47	116.6	63	145.4	79	174.2
16	60.8	32	89.6	48	118.4	64	147.2	80	176.0
17	62.6	33	91.4	49	120.2	65	149.0	81	177.8
18	64.4	34	93.2	50	122.0	66	150.8	82	179.6
19	66.2	35	95.0	51	123.8	67	152.6	83	181.4
20	68.0	36	96.8	52	125.6	68	154.4	84	183.2
21	69.8	37	98.6	53	127.4	69	156.2	85	185.0
22	71.6	38	100.4	54	129.2	70	158.0	86	186.8
23	73.4	39	102.2	55	131.0	71	159.8	87	188.6
24	75.2	40	104.0	56	132.8	72	161.6	88	190.4
25	77.0	41	105.8	57	134.6	73	163.4	89	192.2
26	78.8	42	107.6	58	136.4	74	165.2	90	194.0
27	80.6	43	109.4	59	138.2	75	167.0	91	195.8
28	82.4	44	111.2	60	140.0	76	168.8	92	197.6
29	84.2	45	113.0	61	141.8	77	170.6	93	199.4
30	86.0	46	114.8	62	143.6	78	172.4	94	201.2

Tables and References

Boiling Point of Distillates

Compound	Deg C
Acetone	56.5
Methanol	64.7
Ethyl Acetate	77.1
Ethyl Alcohol	**78.3**
Propyl Alcohol	97.2
Water	**100.0**
Butyl Alcohol	117.5
Amyl Alcohol	137.8
Furfural	161.0

Distillation separates the various chemical compounds produced during the fermentation process, using the differing boiling points to effect the separation. The boiling points at sea level of some of the more important chemicals found in beer, wine and many commercial spirits produced by fermentation with yeast are shown in this table.

These chemicals found in many commercial beverages are, of course, quite happily consumed, sometimes with unfortunate consequences the next morning!

HokiNooki Moonshine method of distillation and filtering alleviates this.

Spirit Hydrometer Correction Table

	20%	30%	40%	50%	60%	70%	80%	90%
10°	22	32	42	52	62	72	82	91
15°	20	30	40	50	60	70	80	90
20°	19	28	38	49	59	69	79	89
25°	17	26	36	47	57	67	77	88
30°	16	24	34	45	55	66	76	87
35°	14	22	32	43	53	64	74	85

Locate the percentage reading across the top row and the temperature down the left column. The resulting actual percentage is read at the intersection of the two. Eg. You measure 60% on your hydrometer, then 20° C on your thermometer. The actual percentage of alcohol is 59%. The percentage error is mainly at the lower measured percentage. As you can see, the greatest correction figures are required lower percentages and highest temperatures. Around 15 to 16 degrees is where most spirit hydrometers (Alcolmeters) are calibrated without any requirement for correction.

Alcohol Dilution Table

Across the top row is the Percentage of our Original Stock Spirit.

Down the left side column is the Desired Percentage of our Spirit.

%	93	90	85	80	75	70	65	60	55	50	45	40
90	3.2	0.0										
85	8.6	5.6	0.0									
80	14	11	5.9	0.0								
75	19	17	12	6.3	0.0							
70	25	22	18	12	6.7	0.0						
65	30	28	23	19	13	7.1	0.0					
60	35	33	29	25	20	14	7.7	0.0				
55	41	39	35	31	27	21	15	8.3	0.0			
50	46	44	41	38	33	28	23	17	9.1	0.0		
45	52	50	47	44	40	36	31	25	18	10	0.0	
40	57	56	53	50	47	43	38	33	27	20	11	0.0
35	62	61	59	56	53	50	46	42	36	30	22	13
30	68	67	65	63	60	57	54	50	45	40	33	25
25	73	72	71	69	67	64	62	58	55	50	44	38

This table will be useful for mixing your spirits to a desired percentage from your high-octane stock. If you have 50% alcohol in stock then look across the top row and locate 50%. Now you desire to dilute this with water to end up with 35%, so drop down to the 35% row by looking at the left column. The 50% (top) to 35% (left side) intersect giving you a figure of 30. This means that you need to add 30% of water and 70% spirit. If your original volume needed is 1000ml then add 300ml of water and 700ml of spirit to make your desired 35% spirit.

Formula used: 100 − (Desired Quantity **X** Desired % ÷ Original %)

Imperial to Metric to US Measurements

Volume

1	Imperial Gallon	4.55	Litre
1	Litre	0.22	Imp. Gallon
1	US Gallon	3.78	Litre
1	Litre	0.26	US Gallon
1	Imperial Pint	568.10	Millilitres
1	US Pint	473.60	Millilitres
1	Imperial Fluid Ounce	28.40	Millilitres
1	US Fluid Ounce	29.60	Millilitres

Weight

1	Pound (lb)	454.00	Grams
1	Ounce (oz)	28.40	Grams
1	Kilogram	2.20	Pounds
1	Gram	0.035	Ounces

Length

1	Inch	25.40	Millimetres
1	Inch	2.54	Centimetres
1	Foot	30.48	Centimetres
1	Centimetre	0.39	Inch
1	Metre	39.37	Inches

Temperature

32°	Fahrenheit (F)	0.00°	Celsius (C)
212°	Fahrenheit (F)	100.00°	Celsius (C)
172.67°	Fahrenheit (F)	78.15°	Celsius (C)

Temperature Formula

{Deg F - 32} X 5 / 9 = Deg C
Deg C X 9 / 5 + 32 = Deg F
Consult the Temperature Conversion Table on page 89.

Specific Gravity

Ethanol SG = 0.92

Definitions of Brewers & Distillers Jargon

Activated Carbon
Ground or crushed charcoal treated with high-pressure super heated steam.

Aging
Time spent in slumber, mellowing.

Airlock
Water filled device that allows bubbling of carbon dioxide to escape without permitting the entering of bacteria or outside air.

Alcometer
A specially calibrated hydrometer to establish the percentage of alcohol contained within water.

Aldehydes
The lighter alcohols than ethyl alcohol as an undesirable by-product of fermentation. They include methanol that evaporates at 65° C.

Amino Acid
A chemical that allows building of proteins.

Amylase
Enzyme used to reduce starches to Dextrin.

Azeotrope
A blend of two liquids into a solution, that when mixed at a certain ratio, will boil at a temperature lower than either of the two original liquids.

Blending
Careful mixing of flavours and spirits to produce a delightful beverage.

Boiling Vessel
A container that is heated with the contents of the fermented Wash of sugar, yeast and water.

Bootlegging
Smuggled bottles of booze that were stored inside the trouser legs of illicit traders.

Bubble Trap
See Fermentation Lock.

Cask
Oak wooden barrel.

Carbohydrates
Sugar based foodstuff.

Condenser
A cooled device that allows heated vapour to be converted back into a liquid.

Dextrin
A gummy substance converted by Diastase enzyme to Maltose.

Dextrose
A simple sugar that is converted to alcohol and carbon dioxide by enzyme Zymase (yeast).

Distillate
The condensed vapour that emerges from the Condenser after distillation.

Distillation
The processes of separating various liquids back into their original state.

Definitions

Enzymes	A microscopic protein that break down complex mixtures of sugars and carbohydrates into a different form.
Ethyl Alcohol	The result of careful fermentation by enzymes into a product that can be consumed socially without poisoning.
Excise Tax	Revenue collected on alcohol and tobacco normally by the department of customs.
Fermentation	The conversion of sugars and carbohydrates into another product such as carbon dioxide and alcohol.
Fermentation Lock	A device to allow carbon dioxide to pass through from the fermentation vessel, but not allow the outside air to enter this vessel.
Fermentation Rate	The elapsed time required to complete Fermentation.
Fermentation Vessel	A container used to ferment the mixture of sugar, yeast, nutrients and water.
Filtering	The process that is employed to purify the distillate after leaving the Still. It removes unwanted lower and higher alcohols than ethyl alcohol.
Fortification	The blending or adding of high percentage spirit to Wine to produce Port and Sherries etc with a higher alcoholic content that can normally be achieved from fermentation.
Fractional Distillation	The process by which various fractions or liquid types that can be extracted using carefully controlled heating and cooling from a complex mixture of liquids.
Fusel Oils	A non-specific name given to a complex range of heavy alcohols with a higher boiling point to that of pure alcohol. At low levels of ethyl alcohol percentage these oils are visible floating on top of the distillate.
Gasohol	A blend of Gasoline and Alcohol used as an alternative fuel for petrol engines in cars.
Heads	The lighter alcohols or fore-shots that emerge before ethyl alcohol during distillation.

Definitions

Heat Belt	An electrical bandage to wrap around your fermentation vessel to raise the temperature during the colder months.
Heat Pad	An electrical heater normally placed underneath the fermentation vessel to maintain a constant temperature during the colder months.
Heat Source	Either gas or electric heating required for the boiling vessel.
HokiNuki	A name used by some elite Moonshiners in days of old gone by.
Hops	A plant leaf used for the production of Beer. It adds a unique flavour.
Hydrometer	A floating device with a calibrated shaft extending from the top of the float to establish the density of a solution.
Malting	A process of converting carbohydrates, such as crushed grain, into Maltose, using enzymes.
Maltose	A sugar that can be converted to Dextrose by the enzyme Maltase.
Mash	Porridge like germinated grain used as a source of sugar and carbohydrates required for fermentation.
Mashing	Process of soaking the grains in water at a controlled temperature in order to accelerate enzyme activity.
Mashing Enzymes	*Alpha amylase* produces un-fermentable sugars at 67 to 70° C and *beta amylase* produces fermentable sugars and works well at 62 to 64° C.
Molasses	A by-product from a sugar mill that is left over from making sugar from sugar cane. It contains around 8% if sugar and a variety of other products that is ideal for producing Rum using fermentation and distillation. It is also often used as stock feed.
Moonshine	The USA name given for illicit alcohol production that was normally produced during the dark moonlight hours. The moon would illuminate the steam surrounding the large illegal distilleries.
Needle Valve	A small Tap or Faucet that will allow minute controllable adjustments to the flow of a liquid.

Definitions

Nutrients	A complex mixture of essential yeast food for the clean fermentation process.
Oaking	A liquid that is added to a spirit blend, and is required to produce a more mellow taste as if it was aged in an oak barrel.
Peat	Partially decomposed vegetable matter found in swamps.
PET	Polyethylene plastic often used for drink bottles.
PH	The Acidity (0 to 7), or Alkaline (7 to 12) level measurement of a solution. A PH of 5.3 to 5.5 is ultimate for the start of Mash fermentation.
Pot Still	A simple still that has no Reflux Column and is used to extract alcohol from a complex solution.
Potable	Drinkable without poisoning.
Purification	See Filtering.
Reflux Column	A column that will selectively control the temperature of vapours and their condensation points to extract a chosen liquid of ethyl alcohol.
Reflux Still	A miniature version of a fractional distillation column, plus a condenser, that is used to selectively extract alcohol at a superior percentage to that of a Pot Still.
Specific Gravity	The measurement of a liquid to ascertain the density of that solution. Water has a density of one.
Spirit	Alcohol or alcoholic blend.
Starch	Carbohydrates formed from long chains of glucose molecules. Broken down by Amylase.
Tails	The remaining solution of heavier alcohols as a by-product of distillation at high temperatures. Often called the feints.
Triac	An electronic device that is used to switch or control the house mains voltage or power. Often used in light dimmers.
Triclover Coupler	A stainless steel method of connecting tubes or pipes with a quick release. Often used in milking machine equipment.

Definitions

Vapour	The invisible evaporated liquid that emerges from a heated solution. Normally a higher temperature than visible steam
Vapour Point	The defined and precise temperature that a liquid will evaporate into a vapour.
Wash	The resultant mixture of sugar, yeast, nutrients and water that will be fermented to produce ethyl alcohol.
Water Flow	The measurement of flowing water in litres per minute through the condenser and Reflux Still to maintain the correct temperature and cooling for efficient distillation.
Watts	A measurement of electrical power. Multiply the voltage by the current (Amps) and your result is watts. 240 Volts X 4.17 Amps = 1000 Watts
Yeast	A microscopic living organism, which excretes enzymes that will convert sugars/glucose into ethyl alcohol and carbon dioxide with enzyme *Zymase*.
Zymase	An enzyme from yeast that converts Dextrose to ethyl alcohol and carbon dioxide.

Photographic Section

Compact Reflux Still

This Stainless Steel Reflux Still measures only 300 mm in height from the top of the 5ltr Pressure cooker. It represents a sample of what the imagination can create for today's small and compact market. It is ideal

for the small home unit because it requires so little space. The heat source could be from your kitchen hotplate as the height allows it to be mounted under the range hood. The thermometer is inserted through a hole located in the rubber bung on the top of the reflux tower.

Common cooling water for both the reflux tower and the internally mounted condenser is contained in the canister mounted towards the top of the tower. 1.5 metres of tubing coiled up inside the canister acts as the cooling condenser. The pressure cooker is available from retail stores.

Large Home Pot Still of Yesteryear

An old Pot Still creation that many Moonshiners assembled in the days of old. It was converted from an old Beer Keg, 18 gallons, and heated using a 4-burner gas system. All burners were operational during initial heating, and then only the two smaller flames were in use during distillation. The lighter drum to the left side contained the condenser and cooling water. It was a coil of 10mm stainless steel tubing measuring 6mtr in length. The small can, situated on the far left, collected spirit at about 40% alcohol by volume. There was no actual temperature monitoring provided.

This Pot Still was used to make HokiNuki Rum, many years ago. Being a Pot Still, instead of a Reflux Still, the quality of the rum was rather dubious to say the least, but the taste was excellent after a time of slumber within large oak barrels. The recipe for the rum included a hefty amount of molasses and chopped up citrus fruit, complete with skins.

It has been known for the Reflux column, from the previous page, to be mounted atop this Beer Keg for finer quality distillation.

List of Drawings and Photographs